Key Stage 2 English Semantics

WORKBOOK **3**

Homonyms
(Homographs & Homophones)

Dr Stephen C Curran
with Warren Vokes

Edited by
Andrea Richardson and Katrina MacKay

This book belongs to

Accelerated Education Publications Ltd

bluff	**press**	**evening**
mole	**bar**	**pitcher**
box	**case**	**date**
boil	**clear**	**rock**

Exercise 1a

1) They waited patiently for the kettle to boil to make a pot of tea.

2) The doctor confirmed that the __________ on her back was not malignant.

3) There is a strong group ______________ that binds them together.

4) Viewers watching the ___________ broadcast saw the events unfold as they happened.

5) His doctor studied the _________ notes before making a diagnosis.

6) Before the aircraft was allowed to _______ , it had to be passed as airworthy.

7) In baseball, the ______________ throws the ball to the batter.

8) "Let's set a ______________ to meet again in August."

9) The team failed to ______________ home the advantage and lost the match.

10) A _________ of nostalgia overcame the war veterans.

Score /10

Exercise 1b

11) The fire spread relentlessly, consuming the dry, parched ______________ .

12) The mayor agreed to ______________ the prizes at the school speech day.

13) She tried to __________ but her friends saw through her ruse.

14) The humble ________ of soap has been replaced with liquid hand wash.

15) Her burnt cakes were __________ hard and completely inedible.

16) It was necessary to pack them in a __________ with layers of protective wrapping.

17) After many years of trial and error they managed to ______________ the process.

18) His attempts to rectify the situation only seemed to ______________ the problem.

19) When the police arrived their first task was to ______________ the area.

20) He hit another six, thus _____________ the score.

Score /10

live
present
wave
spirit
perfect
compound
fly
brush

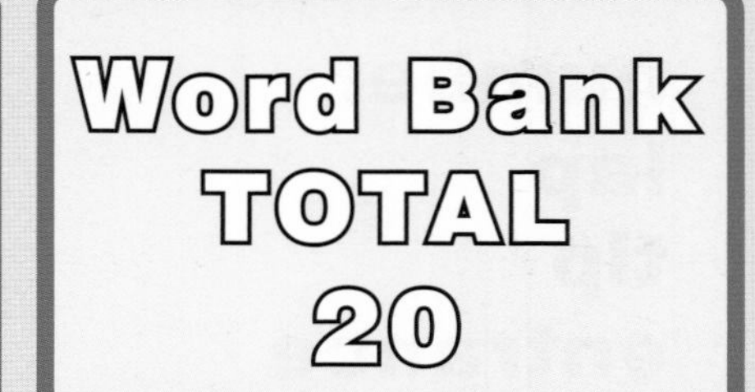

Across

1

1. Enclosed group of buildings.
5. Cliff with a broad face.
6. Transparent.
7. Pus-filled abscess on the skin.
8. Fight with fists.
9. A container.
11. Large single-handled jug.
14. Currently happening.
15. Flawless.
17. Make a home.

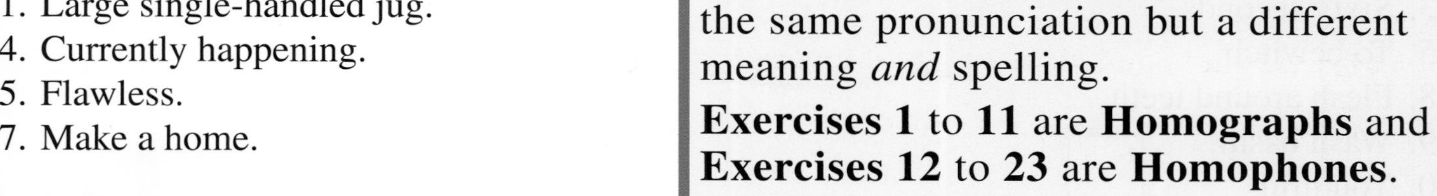

Welcome to: The Wonderful World of Homonyms.

Homonyms may be **Homographs** that have the same spelling but a different meaning, or **Homophones** that have the same pronunciation but a different meaning *and* spelling.

Exercises 1 to **11** are **Homographs** and **Exercises 12** to **23** are **Homophones**.

Use the words shown at the top of each page once only in each question and each puzzle.

Down

2. Massive sea wall.
3. Small oval fruit.
4. Fishhook with feathers.
5. Light contact.
8. Except for.
10. Alcoholic liquor.
11. Device for squeezing something.
12. Late part of the day.
13. Hand signal.
16. Sway to and fro.

Put the mystery letter from the starred square (✳) into box **1** below. Add in the mystery letters from puzzles **2** to **8** then rearrange them to make **Oliver's Mystery Word**.

The clue is **HATS**.

Score
20

Enter your mystery letters here:

1	2	3	4	5	6	7	8

Now rearrange them to make the:

Mystery Word:

number	**count**	**hold**
lap	**minute**	**down**
tip	**project**	**fresh**
entrance	**attribute**	**change**

2

Across

3. Tilt.
5. Cargo space.
6. Formal dance.
8. To take unfair advantage.
10. To add up.
11. Opening in the eye.
13. Sixty seconds.
15. To bewitch.
18. Flesh around teeth.
19. Wash basin.
20. Youthful.

Down

1. Flying mammal.
2. Heavy element.
4. Hurl forward.
7. A characteristic.
9. Direction.
12. Not coarse.
14. Top of thighs.
16. A numeral.
17. Cash.

Score /20

Mystery Letter

bat
gum
ball
exploit
lead
fine
pupil
sink

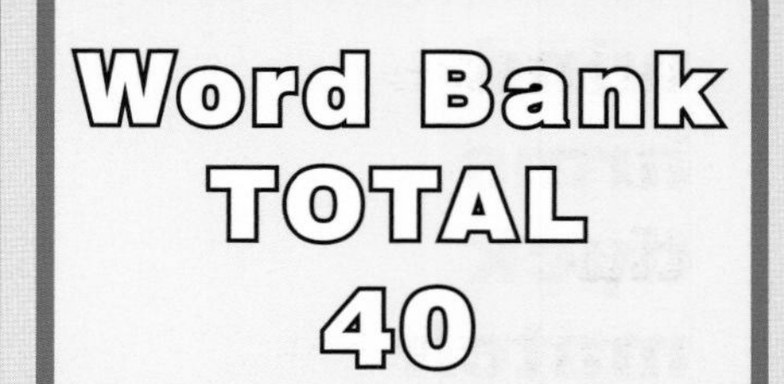

Exercise 2a

1) The _______________ to the cave is only accessible at low tide.

2) She spread the tablecloth made of very _______________ lace on the table.

3) The mallet is a useful tool to _______________ the tent pegs into the dry ground.

4) The sharp _______________ of the javelin makes it a very dangerous weapon.

5) As the swelling increased, his leg became _______________ still.

6) The thirsty cat took little time to _______________ up the milk from the saucer.

7) The _______________ of the eider duck is used in pillows and quilts.

8) He picked up his _______________ and walked purposefully to the crease.

9) She is a wonderful person and her best _______________ is her honesty.

10) He took _______________ of the handle and burst through the door.

Score /10

Exercise 2b

11) Sir Francis Chichester's famous _______________ took nine months and one day.

12) She is a _______________ at Roedean and boards at the school.

13) The greengrocer replaced the tray of oranges with _______________ ones.

14) The sight of chewing _______________ on the pavements always galled him.

15) _______________ Dracula is a ficticious vampire and Transylvanian nobleman.

16) He could not _______________ the situation: he just had to endure it.

17) The microscope allows us to see _______________ details.

18) The Sherpas took the _______________ and the party of climbers followed.

19) Hedgehogs curl into a _______________ to protect themselves from preditors.

20) The digital clock could _______________ the time onto the ceiling.

Score /10

wind	**sewer**	**band**
arms	**refuse**	**subject**
duck	**ring**	**converse**
match	**moped**	**nail**

3

Across

2. To go often to a place.
4. A looped knot.
5. Waste or garbage.
6. Weapons.
8. A strong cloth.
12. Durable circular band.
14. A stick producing fire.
15. To infuriate.
17. A drain for waste.
18. Boy attendant.

Down

1. Abandon an allegiance.
3. A line of things.
4. Instrumental ensemble.
7. Under some authority or control.
9. Polar opposite.
10. Abstain from food.
11. Weighing comparatively little.
13. Moving air.
14. Acted sad or gloomy.
16. Short pointed metal pin.

Mystery Letter

Score

20

page
defect
light
incense
fast
bow
row
frequent

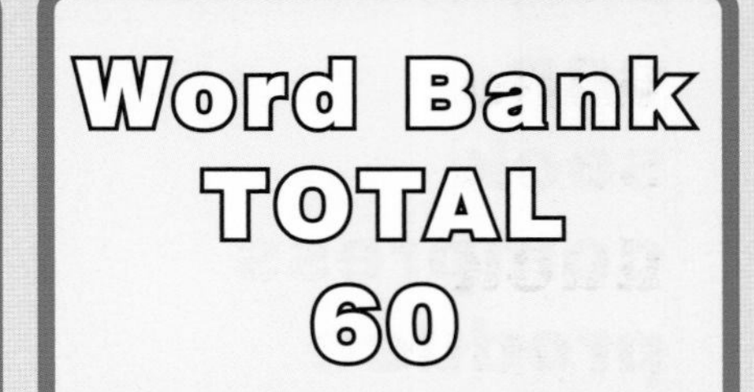

Exercise 3a

1) The cooper fitted the last remaining ______________ around the barrel.

2) The bride and groom are a perfect ______________ .

3) She used an emery board to shape her broken ______________ .

4) At sixteen he could apply for a licence to ride a ______________ .

5) She is an excellent ______________ who stitches everything very neatly.

6) He is a linguist and able to ______________ in French, Spanish and German.

7) "Would you ______________ the hose back onto the hose reel."

8) If he were to ______________ to go with them they may take him by force.

9) It seems that storms and heavy rain are becoming more ______________ .

10) It has a small ______________ , hence the discounted price.

Score ___ / 10

Exercise 3b

11) She used the tannoy to ______________ the supervisor to go to the check-out.

12) Their house always smelled of the ______________ they burned every evening.

13) He was reluctant to discuss the ______________ further as she was becoming upset.

14) He dropped his rifle and raised his ______________ in surrender.

15) The discussion turned ugly and degenerated into a bitter ______________ .

16) He was driven by his love of ______________ cars and a quest for speed.

17) "Somebody must be at home: ______________ the doorbell again!"

18) A small glimmer of ______________ could be seen through the chink in the curtains.

19) He was very tall and had to ______________ under the low branches.

20) She secured the ______________ line before leaving the boat.

Score ___ / 10

can	**loaf**	**overlook**
sock	**accent**	**firm**
compress	**does**	**bass**
produce	**bank**	**prune**

4

Across

1. Hunted animal or bird.
5. To reverse.
6. To move clumsily or heavily.
9. Dismiss as untrue or trivial.
10. To hit hard.
12. Able to.
13. A dried plum.
14. Compact and solid.
15. A spiny-finned fish.
17. A section of the large intestine.
19. The capacity of a container.
20. To batter something.

Down

2. A loud, disturbing noise.
3. Fresh fruit and vegetables.
4. Female deer.
7. Financial services business.
8. To shrink by applying pressure.
11. Be above something.
16. Main emphasis.
18. Spend time lazily.

Score
20

Mystery Letter

quarry
lumber
colon
buffet
back
racket
discount
content

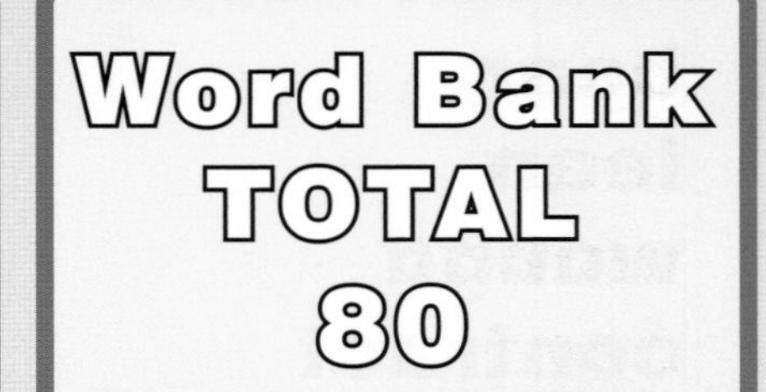

Exercise 4a

1) The sailor used a needle and thread from his "housewife" to darn his _______________ .

2) He refilled the petrol _______________ at the filling station.

3) In America and Canada, felled trees are manufactured into _______________ .

4) The nurse applied a _______________ to stop the bleeding.

5) The company decided to _______________ cars instead of motorcycles.

6) Not _______________ with his house, he used his inheritance to purchase a larger one.

7) The police arrested the criminals involved in the illegal _______________ .

8) He sings in the _______________ section of the choral group.

9) The _______________ on the price of the handbag made it an irresistable bargain.

10) " _______________ it come with a comprehensive guarantee?"

Score / 10

Exercise 4b

11) "Would you prefer a white or brown _______________ ?" asked the baker.

12) All the houses in the locality are built of stone from the nearby _______________ .

13) The family _______________ of solicitors was founded in 1750.

14) Along the river _______________ could be seen the entrances to water rats' burrows.

15) He lived in the south for thirty years but still did not lose his Geordie _______________ .

16) She tried not to _______________ any evidence but her report was incomplete.

17) It took six visits to the osteopath to realign the vertebrae in his lower _______________ .

18) Their holiday included breakfast and dinner from the _______________ .

19) He used a _______________ in the sentence when it should have been a comma.

20) The arborist knew the best way to _______________ the fruit tree.

Score / 10

bear	**learned**	**process**
lean	**yard**	**conduct**
wound	**well**	**pound**
contract	**coordinates**	**intimate**

5

Across

4. The bottom or lowest part.
5. Relate spiritually to something.
6. Enthusiastic admirer.
8. Unit of length.
13. Organises something complex.
14. In good health.
16. Drop of fluid from the eye.
17. Bend or incline.
18. Behaviour.

Down

1. Push in forcibly.
2. Enclosure for stray animals.
3. Large furry animal.
5. To shrink or lessen.
7. A collection of abridged articles.
9. Order back.
10. A series of actions.
11. Past tense of 'learn'.
12. Hint quietly.
14. Injury to body.
15. Somebody with persistent disease.

Mystery Letter

Score

20

invalid
fan
tear
digest
foot
jam
recall
commune

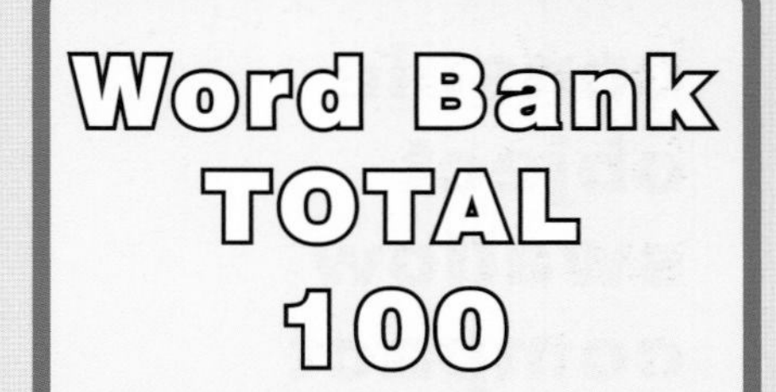

Exercise 5a

1) They had become _______________ friends over the years since their schooldays.

2) The crowd saw the choirboys _______________ from the Home Office to the Cenotaph.

3) The tower of Pisa has a _______________ of 3.99 degrees from vertical.

4) Most kibbutzim in Israel have 200 members within the _______________ .

5) He just managed to stop the car a _______________ short of the hazard.

6) She _______________ the skein of wool into a ball.

7) She could _______________ the pain no longer and took two paracetamol tablets.

8) The navigator entered the _______________ for their destination and they set off.

9) His mother repaired the small _______________ in the knee of his trousers.

10) He continued to _______________ the door while ringing the bell.

Score /10

Exercise 5b

11) At the rear of the terraced cottage is a small _______________ with a washing line.

12) His will has not been witnessed and is therefore _______________ .

13) They dropped a stone into the _______________ but heard no splash from below.

14) After hours of questioning, her interogators _______________ nothing new.

15) Toast and scrambled eggs were easier to _______________ after her sickness.

16) They ordered a pot of tea for two with scones, cream and strawberry _______________ .

17) They signed the _______________ for the house purchase last Wednesday.

18) The old man's _______________ was poor: he did not even recognise his brother.

19) The oscillating _______________ helped to cool the air in the room.

20) Copper is able to _______________ heat and electricity very well.

Score /10

console	**pen**	**mind**
object	**desert**	**close**
swallow	**proceeds**	**putting**
compact	**polish**	**incline**

Exercise 6a

1) He had a ______________ to go for a long walk but the rain put paid to that idea.

2) She bought a new, finer ______________ for her watering can.

3) Many ______________ airmen flew with the RAF during World War II.

4) After closing the shop, the owner ______________ to count the day's takings.

5) It was impossible to ______________ her at her mother's funeral.

6) Reversing sensors have made it much easier to ______________ a car.

7) The first clap of thunder was followed by a ______________ even louder one.

8) She checked she had her make-up ______________ and spectacles in her handbag.

9) The ______________ of the game Monopoly is to bankrupt the other players.

10) She was alerted by a light ______________ on the window pane.

Score /10

Exercise 6b

11) The ______________ was so steep they had to climb rather than walk up it.

12) "You should chew your food more before you ______________ it."

13) The shepherd and his collie dog gathered the sheep into the ______________ .

14) He stole the money from her purse when she ______________ the room.

15) She told a little white ______________ which she thought would not matter.

16) ______________ by is a shop that sells almost everything you may need.

17) The native woman carried the load by ______________ it on her head.

18) He tried to chop the wood but the three ______________ he had were all too blunt!

19) A gust of wind ______________ the dustbin, spilling its contents onto the driveway.

20) The camel is often referred to as the ship of the ______________ .

Score /10

rose	**upset**	**Word Bank TOTAL 120**
lie	**tap**	
axes	**second**	
left	**park**	

Across

6

1. Placing something.
4. Publicly owned area of land.
6. A 60th of one minute.
7. Short and sturdy.
10. Small songbird.
14. Reddish-pink.
16. To be likely to act.
18. To totally abandon a place.
19. Departed.

Down

2. A dramatic change.
3. Money obtained from a transaction.
4. Make smooth or glossy.
5. A water valve.
8. To temporarily watch over.
9. Alliances.
11. A falsehood.
12. To write something.
13. Control panel.
15. Something visible or tangible.
17. To cover an opening.

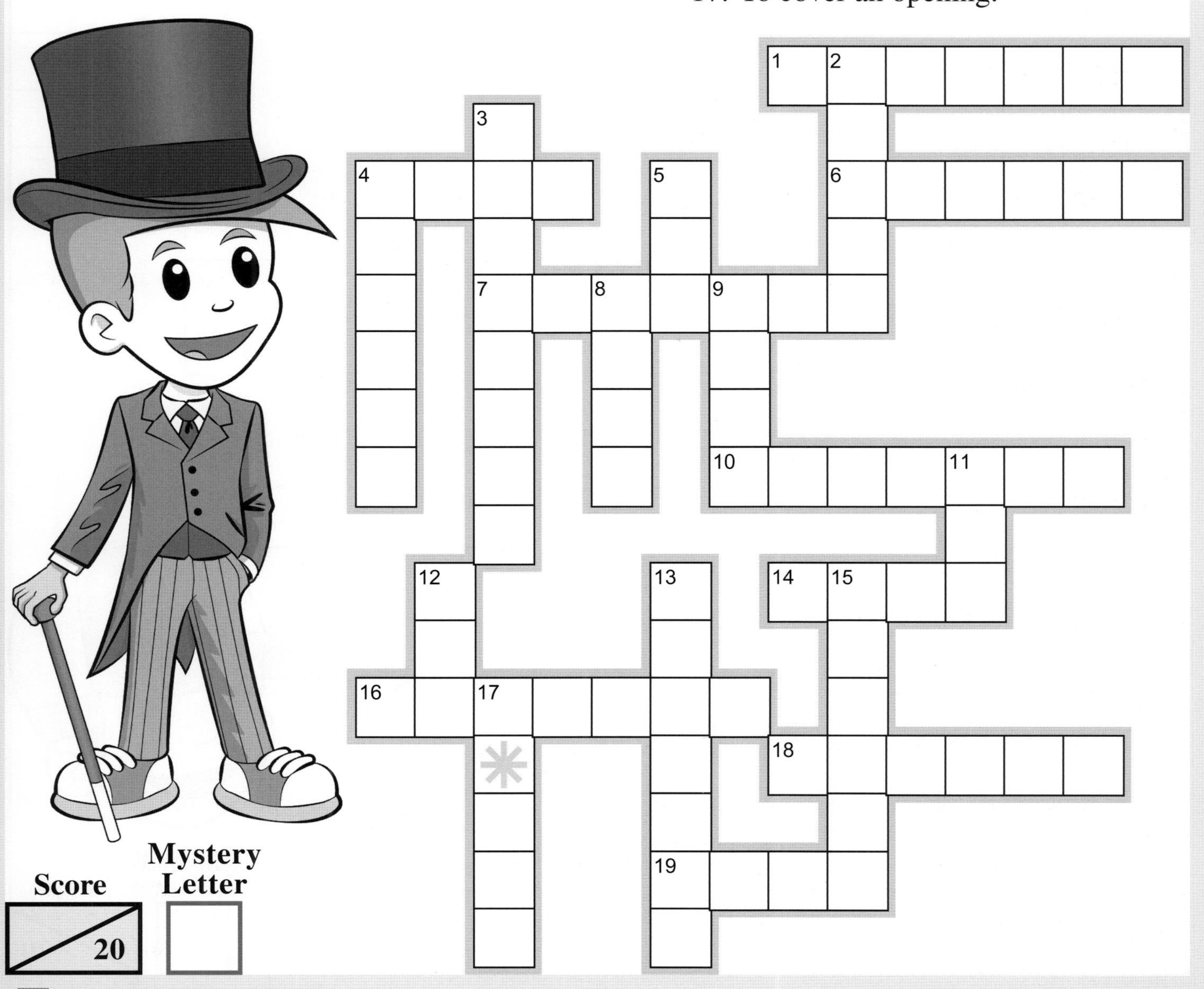

sign	**hamper**	**frank**
novel	**sentence**	**kid**
scale	**against**	**loom**
bolt	**buckle**	**harbour**

7

Across

3. Lightning flash.
7. Weaving apparatus.
8. Punishment allocation.
9. New and original.
10. In contact by leaning or resting alongside.
13. Meat cooked quickly and lightly.
17. To impede.
18. Public waiting room.
19. Young goat.

Down

1. Sticky substance obtained from tar.
2. Instrument with graduated markings.
3. A bulge, bend or kink.
4. Write one's name.
5. Ship's crew.
6. Computer video display.
11. Gas around a celestial body.
12. Make a deep hole.
14. Safe place of refuge.
15. Bent wire to fasten papers.
16. Open and blunt.

atmosphere	**bore**
pitch	**monitor**
staple	**rare**
lounge	**company**

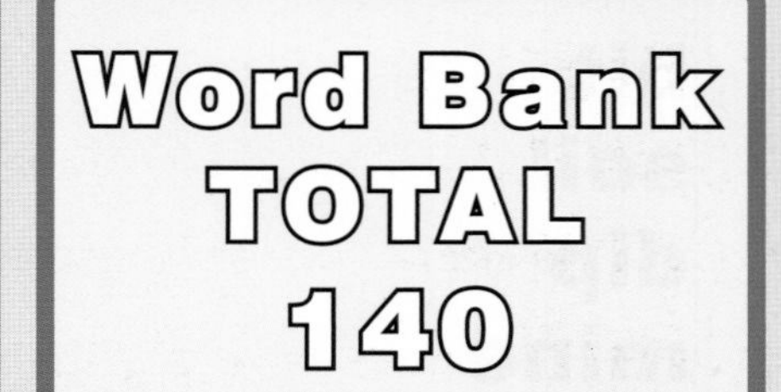

Exercise 7a

1) As soon as she walked into the room she sensed the _______________ was tense.

2) Her _______________ was a story of two soldiers on the Western Front in World War I.

3) He need not have feared for his safety: he was in good _______________ .

4) The nurse checked him every 15 minutes to _______________ his condition.

5) The ____________ on the envelope confirmed the postage had been prepaid.

6) It is _______________ the law to own a firearm without a licence.

7) After her ordeal, she would always _____________ a grudge towards her tormentors.

8) "Don't just _______________ around the house, go out for some fresh air!"

9) She spread the rug, opened the _______________ and laid out their picnic.

10) He tried to _______________ her he had won the lottery.

Score ___ / 10

Exercise 7b

11) The warship seemed to _______________ menacingly only a mile from the shore.

12) Knowledge of grammar and parsing is required to construct a _____________ .

13) The hikers decided to _______________ their tent and rest for the night.

14) He is so fit, it is _______________ for him to be ill.

15) The foreign ministers took their turn to sit at the table and _______________ the treaty.

16) The lesson was a complete ___________ and she found it difficult to concentrate.

17) "Don't ____________ your food! There is no rush to finish the meal!"

18) Foreigners believed roast beef with Yorkshire pudding was our ______________ diet.

19) The mountaineers would have to hurry to ____________ the north face before the storm.

20) The _____________ broke and he could not fasten his belt.

Score ___ / 10

bit	**fire**	**state**
soil	**pawn**	**like**
dip	**hard**	**spring**
mine	**hail**	**fork**

Exercise 8a

1) "You can't just _______________ a decision like that on me!"

2) She had to _______________ her jewellery to raise some cash.

3) Many acting careers have begun with just a _______________ part in a film or play.

4) She has been a friend of _______________ since we were at school together.

5) Top of the _______________ tonight is a famous tenor.

6) He left her a _______________ to remind her to meet him at his office.

7) The police report showed there was a _______________ of burglaries last month.

8) Whatever the weather, they went for a quick _______________ in the sea every morning.

9) She shouted and raised her arm to _______________ a taxi.

10) The gunnery officer gave the order to open _______________ .

Score /10

Exercise 8b

11) The plumber used a _______________ to remove the burrs from the pipe.

12) She used flour, milk and eggs to make the _______________ .

13) The farmer tilled the _______________ with a harrow before planting the crop.

14) "If you _______________ , I'll join you later and we can have a chat then."

15) They poured and levelled the concrete base then left it overnight to go _______________ .

16) Their cold and hungry dog was in a dreadful _______________ when it was rescued.

17) My _______________ reaction was panic; then I realised the ride was quite safe.

18) He finally lost his _______________ , shouted at them and stormed out of the meeting.

19) It took them all morning to _______________ over the soil on their allotment.

20) "Take _______________ of the children while I talk to their parents."

Score /10

initial	**batter**
charge	**note**
temper	**rash**
file	**bill**

Word Bank TOTAL 160

Across

8

2. To make dirty or stained.
6. Such as.
8. An ordered collection of papers.
9. Lowest value chess piece.
11. A hidden explosive.
12. To hit repeatedly.
15. Pile of burning fuel.
16. Pellets of ice.
17. Difficult or awkward.

Down

1. A bird's beak.
2. Water source.
3. Express in words.
4. To lower, then raise again.
5. To harden metal by heating and cooling.
7. The first letter of a name.
10. To observe something.

Down (continued)

12. Bridle mouthpiece.
13. Thoughtless and impetuous.
14. Attack at a rush.
15. Split into two branches.

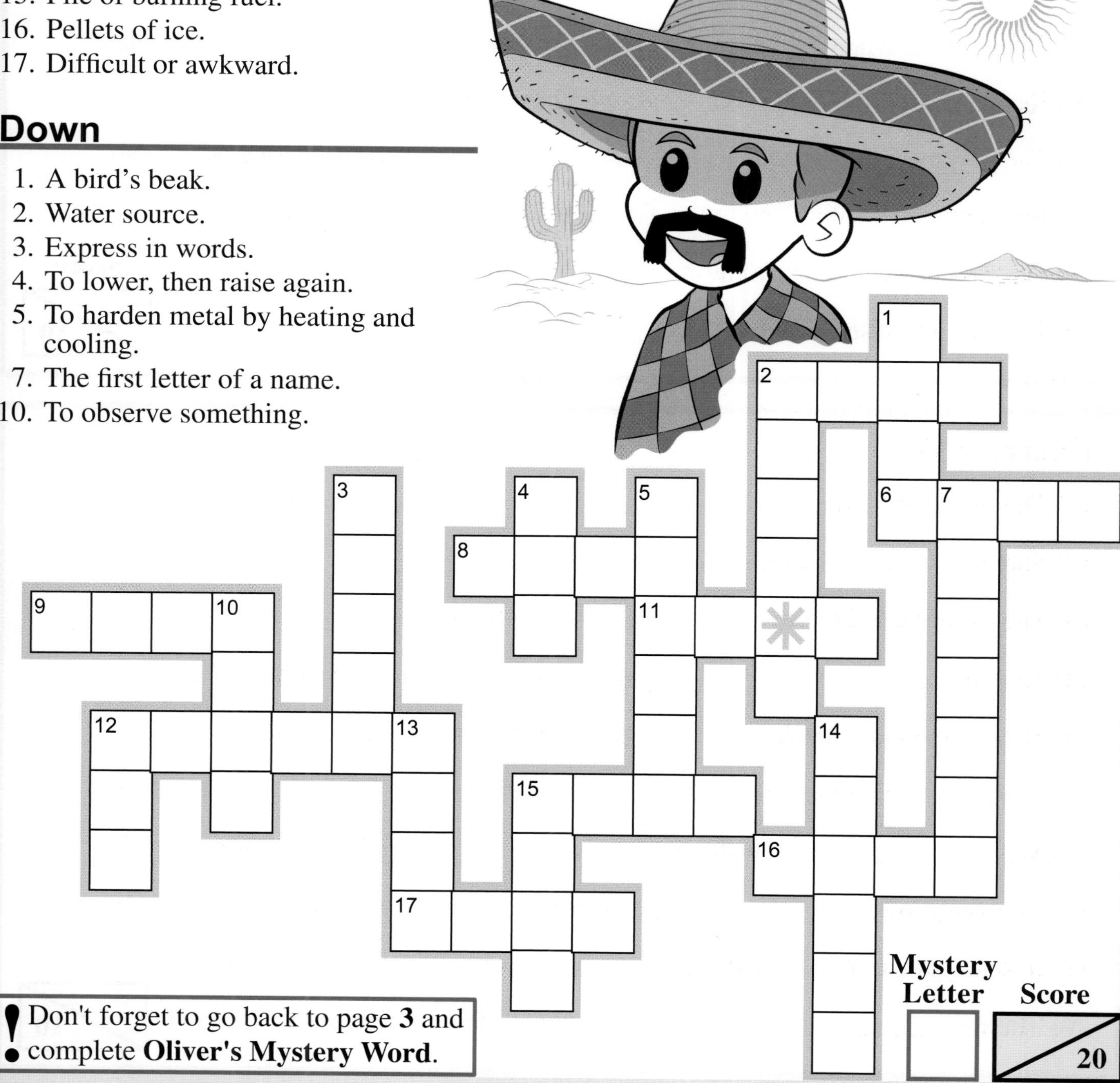

Mystery Letter

Score /20

! Don't forget to go back to page **3** and complete **Oliver's Mystery Word**.

plain	**fuse**	**grave**
ear	**periodical**	**chest**
bowl	**might**	**spare**
flounder	**saw**	**spruce**

Exercise 9a

1) The captain's cabin is located in the _______________ of the ship.

2) They stood on the deck to watch a _______________ of dolphins race past.

3) She uses herbs, spices and salt to _______________ the dish.

4) Strong winds and heavy seas caused the ship to _______________ on the rocks.

5) Panic sets in when a mixture of emotions and sensations _______________ together.

6) As he is only fifteen, the court deals with him as a _______________ .

7) _______________ brown envelopes usually contain bills or tax demands.

8) He would _______________ down the motorway right on the speed limit.

9) His old head contains a rich _______________ of memories of his time at sea.

10) Lumberjacks use a cross-cut ___________ to fell trees.

Score /10

Exercise 9b

11) She graduated from the piano to playing the _____________ in church.

12) Guy Fawkes and his fellow conspirators met to _______________ the Gunpowder Plot.

13) Deep sea divers discovered the sunken ship in its watery _______________ .

14) I carry a set of _______________ bulbs in my car when I travel abroad.

15) He ordered his monthly _______________ from the local newsagent.

16) A meal in a restaurant before seeing a show makes a _______________ night out.

17) A lick of paint and new wallpaper will soon _______________ up the room.

18) "I thought we _______________ get together and go for a walk at the weekend."

19) A deep _____________ and narrow waist give the greyhound its distinctive silhouette.

20) The farmer checked a single ___________ of wheat for parasites.

Score /10

minor	**terrific**
organ	**stern**
hatch	**season**
store	**school**

Word Bank TOTAL 180

9

Across

2. A lifting door.
5. An evergreen tree of the pine family.
8. To train or instruct somebody in a specific skill.
9. Flat expanse of land.
11. Rigid, strict and uncompromising.
12. Relatively small in quantity, size, or degree.
13. Organ of hearing and balance.
14. Solemn and serious in manner.
15. Mechanical or electrical detonator.
16. A round open dish.
18. Past tense of 'see'.

Down

1. Put away for future use.
3. Traditional division of the year.
4. Great power or influence.
6. Strong rectangular box.
7. An edible flatfish.
9. Recurring or reappearing from time to time.
10. Very great in size, force or degree.
11. To treat somebody leniently.
17. Body part with a specific function.

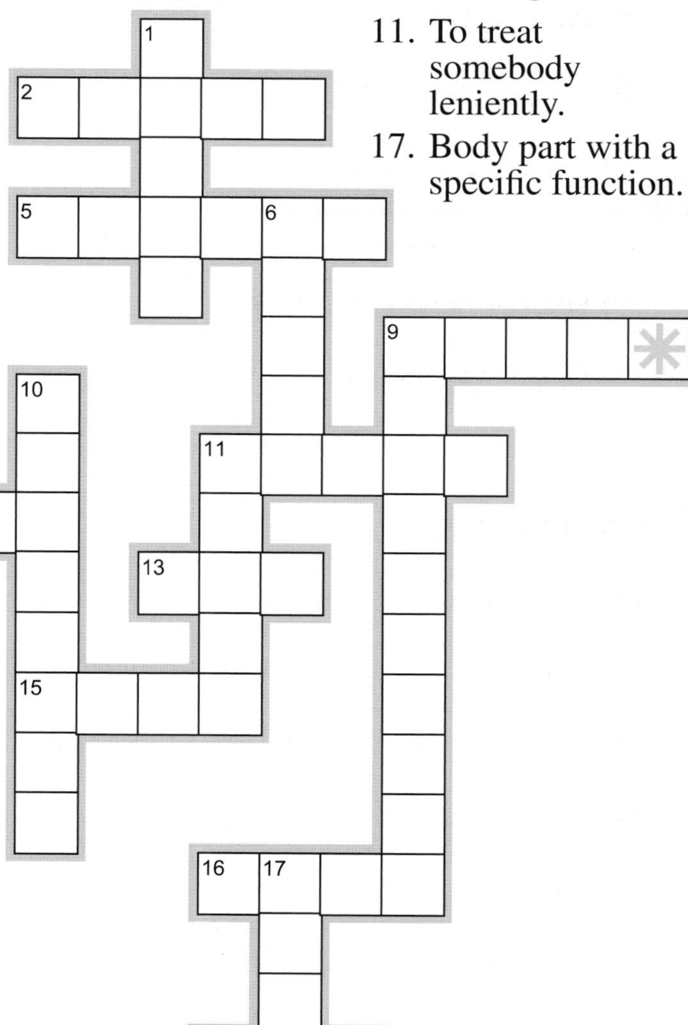

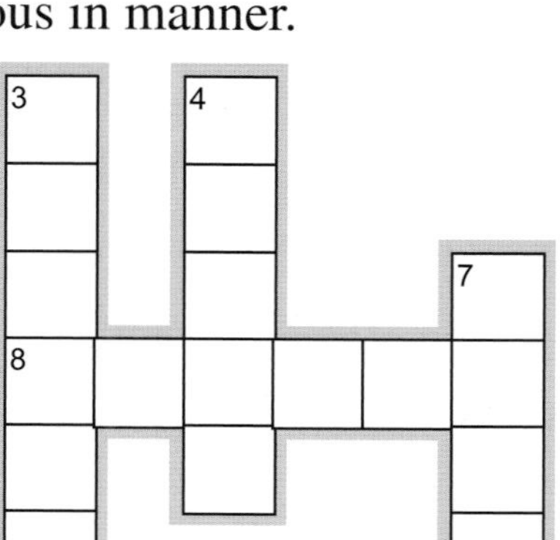

Put the mystery letters from the starred squares (✳) from puzzles **9** to **15** into their numbered box below, then rearrange them to make **Kate's Mystery Word**.

The clue is a **GREAT WOMAN**.

Enter your mystery letters:

9	10	11	12	13	14	15

Now rearrange them to make the:

Mystery Word:

Score /20

sole	**spell**	**watch**
fence	**shed**	**temple**
handle	**board**	**ship**
strike	**suit**	**mint**

Across

10

1. A fluid with substance dissolved it in.
3. To fight with an épée.
8. To deal or cope with.
10. To keep a lookout.
11. To embark.
13. In accordance with the rules.
14. The chorus in a song.
16. A building for worship.
18. To look good on somebody.
19. A short period.

Down

2. Not on time.
4. To train an athlete or other sportsperson.

Down (continued)

5. Only.
6. A small storage structure.
7. A lifting machine.
9. A work stoppage as a protest.
12. To make coins.
15. A symbol representing a number.
17. A section cut from a tree's trunk or branch.
19. To transport over water.

Mystery Letter

Score

/20

solution
coach
fair
late
figure
crane
log
refrain

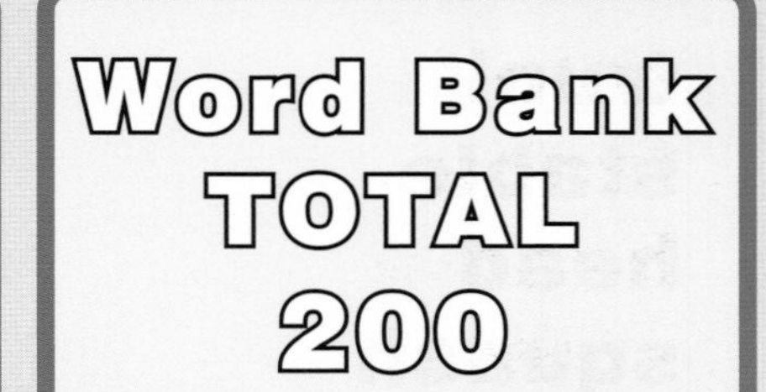

Exercise 10a

1) The bank's computer will ______________ every transaction on your account.

2) Although normally affecting children, the illness may ______________ at any age.

3) The ______________ to the puzzle is fairly easy to solve.

4) Her loss of earnings did not ______________ in the tribunal's conclusions.

5) The floodlights ______________ a brilliant light that illuminates the cathedral.

6) Increased house prices could ______________ disaster for aspiring homeowners.

7) He took his ______________ back to the jewellers to have a new strap fitted.

8) The gold state ______________ weighs four tons and is drawn by eight horses.

9) Her charges for ______________ and lodgings seem very reasonable.

10) It took all her willpower to ______________ from slapping him.

Score /10

Exercise 10b

11) His ______________ grandfather left a substantial legacy.

12) It is customary to serve ______________ sauce to accompany roast lamb.

13) With a ______________ wind behind them their yacht seemed to skim over the water.

14) He turned his head away but the stone hit his ______________ .

15) The crew of the ______________ were very attentive to the passengers' needs.

16) The show-jumper's horse knocked down only one ______________ , scoring 3 faults.

17) The knight's ______________ of armour protected him against swords and arrows.

18) She could not ______________ her neck sufficiently to see over the crowd.

19) She turned the ______________ of the wringer and fed the clothes through the rollers.

20) There is a large hole in the ______________ of his shoe.

Score /10

trunk	**bark**	**patient**
stable	**cobble**	**cabinet**
head	**kind**	**right**
squash	**game**	**reservation**

Exercise 11a

1) On the beach she found a _______________ that had fallen from the cliffs above.

2) He telephoned the restaurant to make a _______________ for dinner.

3) The magician's trick was to _______________ the card unseen by the audience.

4) It took them the whole day to clear the _______________ from the attic.

5) "Well, it's a _______________ of shelter but it's very poorly constructed."

6) He really enjoys eating _______________ , especially venison, rabbit and pheasant.

7) His _______________ comments are often offensive although he intends no malice.

8) The receptionist asked the next _______________ to go through to see the doctor.

9) The mason used a club hammer and pointer to _______________ the stone.

10) The excited children boarded the _______________ to fly to Spain.

Score /10

Exercise 11b

11) In the room is a large _______________ displaying all his sporting trophies.

12) The sergeant would _______________ out his orders to the soldiers.

13) He _______________ home every day at 8.30am and walks to the station.

14) So many people tried to _______________ into the lift that the doors would not close.

15) They packed the large _______________ ready for the voyage.

16) The equerry ordered the soldiers to _______________their horses.

17) He is the tallest among his _______________ group.

18) They failed to _______________ in the right direction and were completely lost.

19) "You're not holding the thing by the _______________ end!"

20) His son's strength was _______________ to his own.

Score /10

incomparable	**dress**
blunt	**peer**
junk	**leaves**
plane	**palm**

Word Bank TOTAL 220

11

Across

2. The obverse of a coin.
5. The upper body.
7. To make or repair shoes.
10. A competitive activity with rules.
11. East, when facing north.
12. A tool for smoothing wood.
13. A vegetable of the gourd family.
14. Not sharp.
17. To look very closely or hard.
18. Government leader's advisers.
19. Flat-bottomed Chinese boat.

Down

1. A limiting condition to an agreement.
3. Woman's one-piece garment.
4. Unique.
6. Foliage.
8. Steady and not liable to change.
9. A tropical tree with fronds.
12. Able to endure waiting.
15. To graze the skin.
16. Having a compassionate nature.

heal	**dough**	**plum**
saver	**made**	**wail**
might	**threw**	**leach**
wet	**mail**	**war**

Across

12

4. To enjoy something unhurriedly.
5. A large marine mammal.
7. Past tense of 'wear'.
8. Tiny eight-legged creature.
9. From beginning to end.
13. A German sausage.
15. A narrow flowerbed.
17. Recipient of hospitality.
18. Hit with a sharp blow.

Down

1. True vertical position.
2. Used to express, tiredness, relief, surprise or disgust.
3. Relating to men or boys.

Down (continued)

6. Back part of shoe or sock.
7. To sharpen a tool or weapon.
8. Woman servant.
10. To sit someone elsewhere.
11. To leap or skip playfully.
12. Hinged barrier across a gap.
14. A blood-sucking worm.
16. Mature female deer, rabbit or goat.

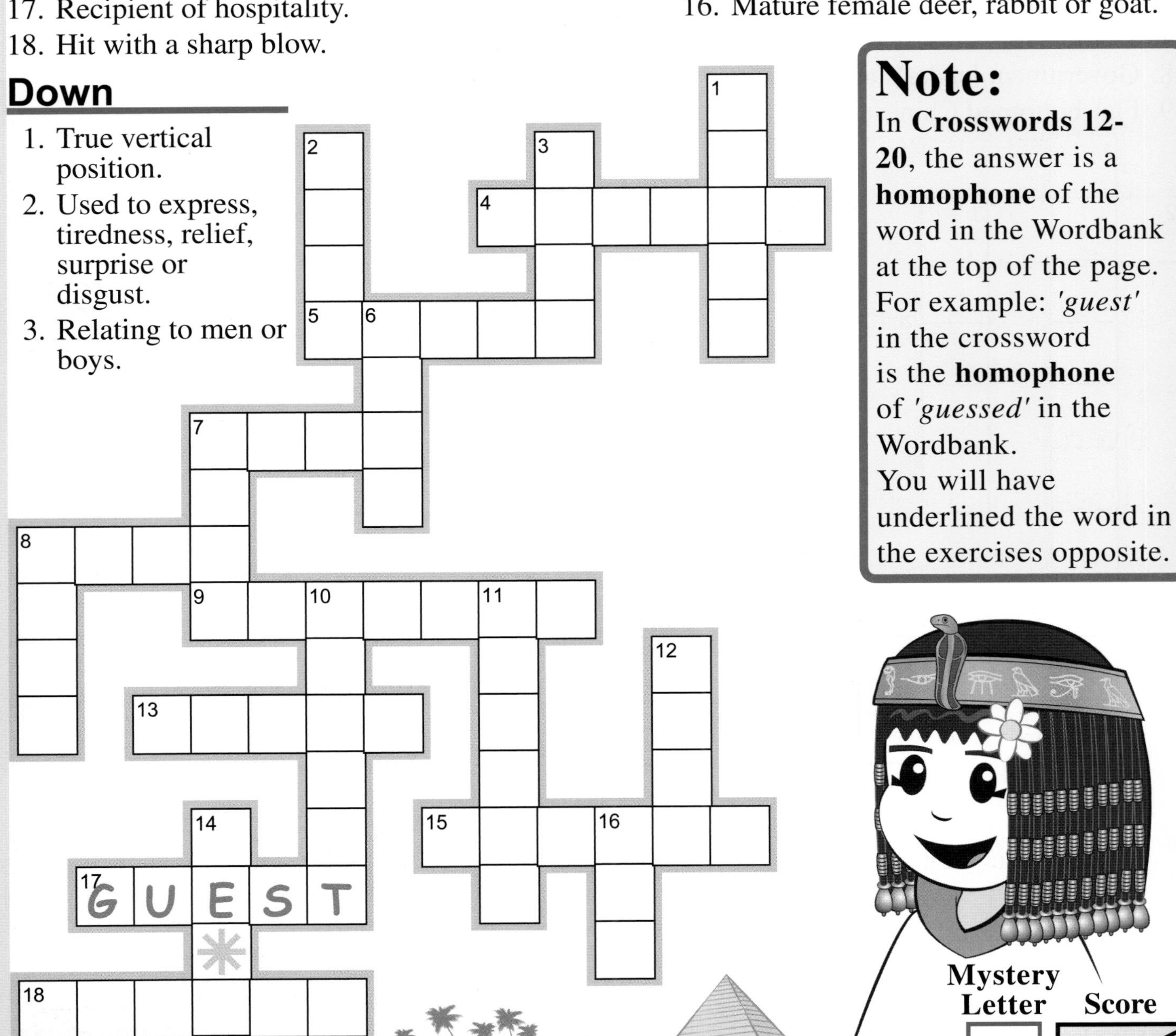

Note:

In **Crosswords 12-20**, the answer is a **homophone** of the word in the Wordbank at the top of the page. For example: *'guest'* in the crossword is the **homophone** of *'guessed'* in the Wordbank. You will have underlined the word in the exercises opposite.

wax
guessed
gamble
boarder
gait
worst
receipt
few

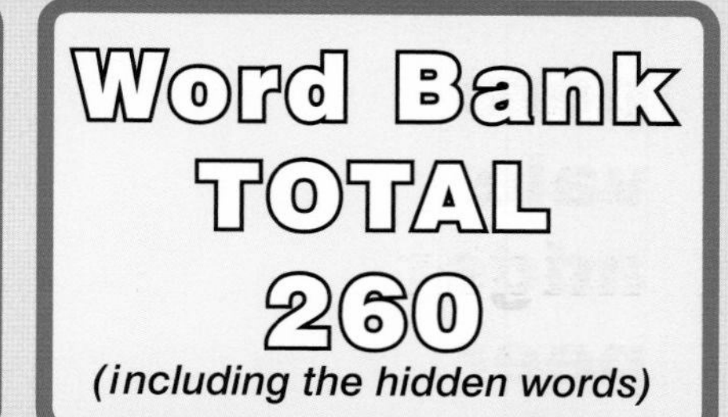

Exercise 12a

Underline the **incorrect word** and write the correct **homophone**.

1) He did not know the answer but he guest correctly. guessed
2) There were very phew loaves left in the baker's shop by lunchtime. ______________
3) The outcome of wore is never certain and always unpredictable. ______________
4) He was a keen savour and put away at least £20 each month. ______________
5) The horse's gate was checked by the vet who found it was slightly lame. ______________
6) She felt it was time to increase the rent paid by her border. ______________
7) The whale of the police car's siren could be heard approaching. ______________
8) It is the wurst tasting sausage I have ever eaten! ______________
9) Kneading the doe properly is the secret of breadmaking. ______________
10) She asked the cashier for a reseat for her purchase. ______________

Score /10

Exercise 12b

11) She has a plumb job working in the chocolate factory. ______________
12) Using only a knife, he maid beautiful carvings from plain driftwood. ______________
13) It was whet outside and she needed her umbrella. ______________
14) He is known to gambol on the horses but he never seems to win. ______________
15) He through the ball for his dog that always retrieved it. ______________
16) I'm planning to go out tonight but I mite change my mind. ______________
17) Not having a letterbox, he had to collect his male from the sorting office. ______________
18) He used a solvent to leech the soluble material from the mixture. ______________
19) Long ago, letters were made secure using sealing whacks. ______________
20) His wound was deep and took a long time to heel. ______________

Score /10

pore	**dual**	**hangar**
vale	**maize**	**presence**
adds	**faint**	**rays**
peer	**medal**	**moan**

Exercise 13a

1) The battered war plane was wheeled into the hanger to be repaired. _______________

2) She felt dizzy and sick but desperately tried not to feint. _______________

3) After fifteen minutes in the bath, every pour in his body felt open. _______________

4) The ship tied up in its birth and the crew lowered the gangplank. _______________

5) The squirrel prepared for the winter by burying its horde of nuts. _______________

6) Astrologers use a radio telescope to pier into the universe. _______________

7) Maze is a cereal crop that originated in South America. _______________

8) The speed limit on motorways and duel carriageways is 70 mph. _______________

9) Wildlife photographers tract the elephants through the forest. _______________

10) They staid in a five star hotel for the weekend. _______________ Score

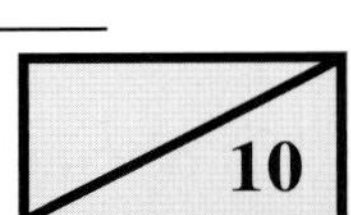

Exercise 13b

11) Her goal is to win a gold meddle at the Olympic Games. _______________

12) The rescue team searched over hill and veil for the missing hikers. _______________

13) He hid his treacherous intentions under the guys of friendship. _______________

14) Exceptionally high tides and heavy seize breached the flood defences. _______________

15) "He's never happy: all he does is mown about everything." _______________

16) The persistent rain adze to the risk of flooding on low-lying land. _______________

17) Building sights sprung up everywhere to meet the demand for housing. _______________

18) "Martial the party's supporters and prepare for the general election!" _______________

19) Dust particles danced in raze of sunlight streaming into the room. _______________

20) Their presents is requested at the board meeting. _______________ Score

marshal
sites
tracked
guise

hoard
seas
berth
stayed

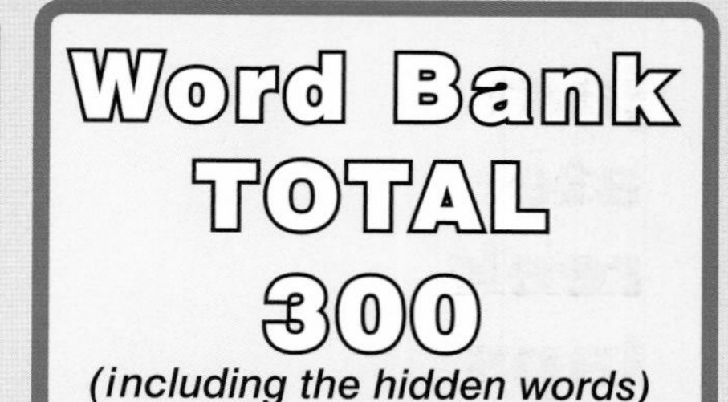

13

Across

2. To interfere.
3. Sedate and settled in habits or temperament.
5. To completely destroy a place.
6. Gifts.
7. Men (informal).
10. A vertical structural support.
12. Process of being born.
14. Suitable for soldiers or war.
15. An area of land or water.
16. Take hold of something.
17. Formal fight over a matter of honour.

Down

1. A woodworking tool.
2. Cut down.
4. A nail or hook from which something may be hung.
6. Make something flow.
8. Sees something.
9. Face covering worn by women.
11. A deceptive move or action.
13. A large group of people.
14. A confusing network of paths.

Score
20

Mystery Letter

jam	**sighs**	**incidence**
ate	**summary**	**overseas**
reek	**lead**	**pail**
laps	**hole**	**rows**

14

Across

1. Entire.
3. The amount, scope, or degree of something.
5. Prickly shrub with ornamental flowers.
10. Description of warm and dry seasonal weather.
11. One more than 7 and one fewer than 9.
12. Something spiral-shaped.
16. Simple and substantial food.
17. A gap in continuity.
19. Showed the way to others.
20. Forbidden.

Down

2. Supervises.
4. Events.
6. Upright support of a door or window frame.
7. Heaviness.
8. Once a week.
9. Cause something violent and destructive.
13. Fit and strong.
14. Make a structure by joining parts.
15. Lacking in colour or intensity.
18. To remove the outer layer.

band
billed
pear
wait
hail
fair
weakly
whirl

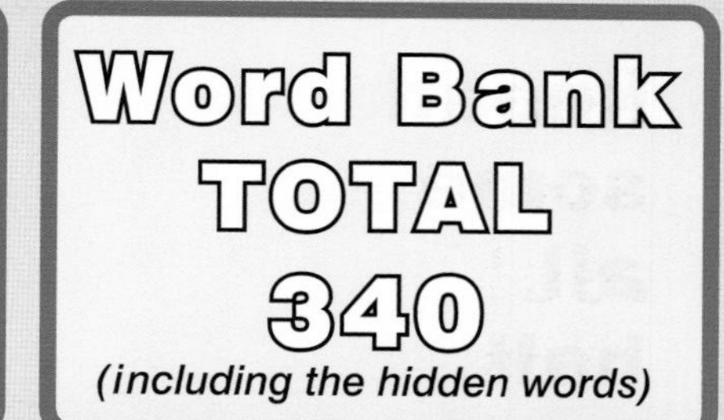

Exercise 14a

1) They are selling all they have and moving oversees to warmer climes. ______________

2) The water at the edge of the lake lapse gently against the shoreline. ______________

3) Rose of back-to-back cottages were a feature of Victorian inner cities. ______________

4) Fermented pare juice is used to produce an alcoholic perry. ______________

5) She asked the hotel doorman to hale a taxi for her. ______________

6) So much information was imparted that it made her head whorl. ______________

7) He has fare skin, so he takes care to use plenty of sun screen. ______________

8) Digging the whole took much longer than the time spent refilling it. ______________

9) The roadworks caused a half mile traffic jamb. ______________

10) She half-filled the pale with milk from the cow. ______________

Score
/10

Exercise 14b

11) During their journey they eight the sandwiches their mother had made. ______________

12) She told her daughters to weight on the corner and not to cross the road. ______________

13) He build his customers every month for the work he had carried out. ______________

14) The workmen replaced the led piping with copper. ______________

15) Size of relief could be heard when the opposition failed to score. ______________

16) The weather forecast followed the news summery. ______________

17) The incidents of part-time working varies across the country. ______________

18) The kitchen fire caused the whole house to wreak of smoke. ______________

19) He replied to the advert for a drummer to join the banned. ______________

20) "I'm fine," she said as she nodded weekly. ______________

Score
/10

knead
some
ail
hall

chews
caster
bean
cheap

stile
links
succour
wood

Exercise 15a

1) The verdict brought no sucker to the victims of his crimes. _______________

2) In every race there is only won winner. _______________

3) The tents and food aid brought sum relief to the refugees. _______________

4) Bread making requires the baker to need the dough well. _______________

5) "Wipe your feet on the doormat in the haul before walking in." _______________

6) The child left the green been on her plate and refused to eat it. _______________

7) Modern drugs cure or relieve many diseases that ale human beings. _______________

8) A ruminant is a hoofed animal that choose the cud. _______________

9) "Play for me again the cord of E*b* minor." _______________

10) The navel display at Portsmouth is not to be missed. _______________

Score /10

Exercise 15b

11) The dry would caught and burned fiercely. _______________

12) In the 19th century the poet, Keats, wrote 'Owed on a Grecian Urn'. _______________

13) It looked too cheep to sell for such an enormous sum. _______________

14) The Panama Canal lynx the Pacific and Atlantic Oceans._______________

15) They climbed over the style to continue along the footpath. _______________

16) A castor on the chair is broken and needs to be replaced. _______________

17) Two diamond shaped pips below a crown denote the rank of kernel. _______________

18) The ball-boy throes the ball to the tennis player for her to serve. _______________

19) He has severe burns that require a skin graphed. _______________

20) The drummer hit the symbol on the off-beat. _______________

Score

cymbal
naval
chord
colonel
throws
graft
one
ode

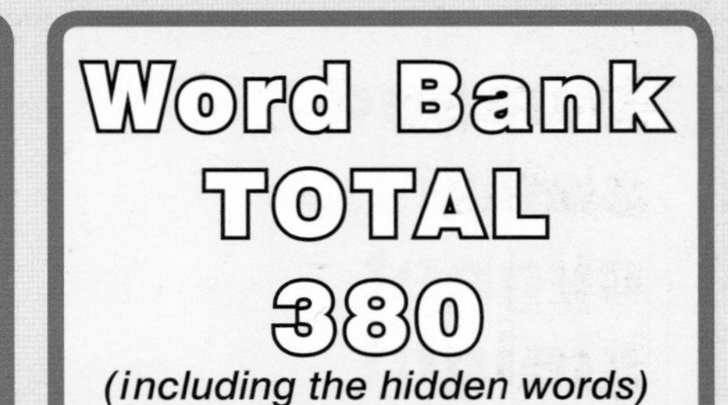

Across

15

1. Brown oily aromatic substance.
4. The central part.
6. A shoot growing from a root.
9. String or rope.
10. Pull or drag something.
14. Decide from a range of different options.
15. Total amount.
16. Require.
17. Used in making a polite request.

Down

1. Sound made by a young bird.
2. Was financially in debt to somebody.
3. Alcoholic drink.
5. Hollow on the surface of the stomach.
6. Way of writing or performing.

Down (continued)

7. Data was added to a chart.
8. Effects of severe physical pain.
11. Past participle of 'be'.
12. Achieved victory.
13. Something that represents something else.
18. A short-tailed wild cat with tufted ears.

! Don't forget to go back to page **19** and complete **Kate's Mystery Word**.

Mystery Letter

Score 20

trussed
sail
cygnet
sleight
choir
pride
soared
pole
miners
blew
brewed
roll

Exercise 16a

1) Emerging from the pit, the minors' faces were black with coal dust. _______________

2) She raised the spoon to her lips and blue on it to cool the soup. _______________

3) Good news on the economy and the stock market sword. _______________

4) They built a four story house on the site of the bungalow. _______________

5) He asked the referee to brush the bays on the snooker table. _______________

6) They all held their breath: it was a tents moment. _______________

7) The heat from the blaze was so intents that no-one could approach. _______________

8) Lewis Clarke became the youngest person to ski-trek to the South Poll. _____________

9) The crocodile's jaws were securely trust with a large elastic band. _______________

10) To repair the windmill's sale was a difficult task. _______________

Score /10

Exercise 16b

11) The pair of swans are very protective of their only signet. _______________

12) After his skis flew off he began to role down the slope at high speed. _______________

13) Porridge with honey is the only breakfast serial he will eat. _______________

14) The crew prepared to gibe the clipper away from the wind. _______________

15) Details of braking news scrolls across the bottom of the screen. _______________

16) Fields of lavender in the south of France are a cite for sore eyes. _______________

17) With a deft slight of hand the magician palmed the card. _______________

18) The scandal brood for several weeks before the story broke. _______________

19) It was her indefatigable sense of pried that spurred her on. _______________

20) Every Sunday he sings in the church quire. _______________

Score

storey **breaking**
intense **sight**
cereal **baize**
jibe **tense**

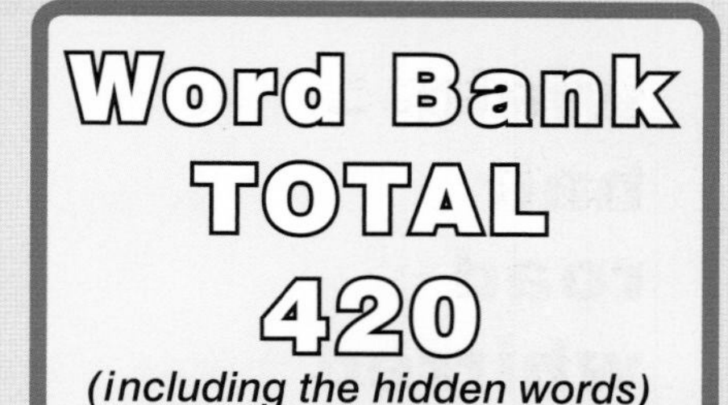

16

Across

1. A survey of the public.
2. The colour of a cloudless sky.
3. A mocking remark.
5. Factual or fictional narrative.
6. Very small in size, degree, amount, or importance.
9. Slowing or stopping a machine or vehicle.
11. An animal's or bird's young.
12. Confidence and reliance.
16. A story published or broadcast in parts.
17. One twentieth of a ream of paper.
18. A small seal.

Down

1. Opened using leverage.
2. Areas or compartments used for a particular purpose.
4. Plans or purposes.
7. Hand-held, long-bladed weapon.
8. Not legally adults.
10. Opportunity to buy goods at a discount.
13. An acting part.
14. Collapsible, movable, fabric shelters.
15. To name somebody in a court case.

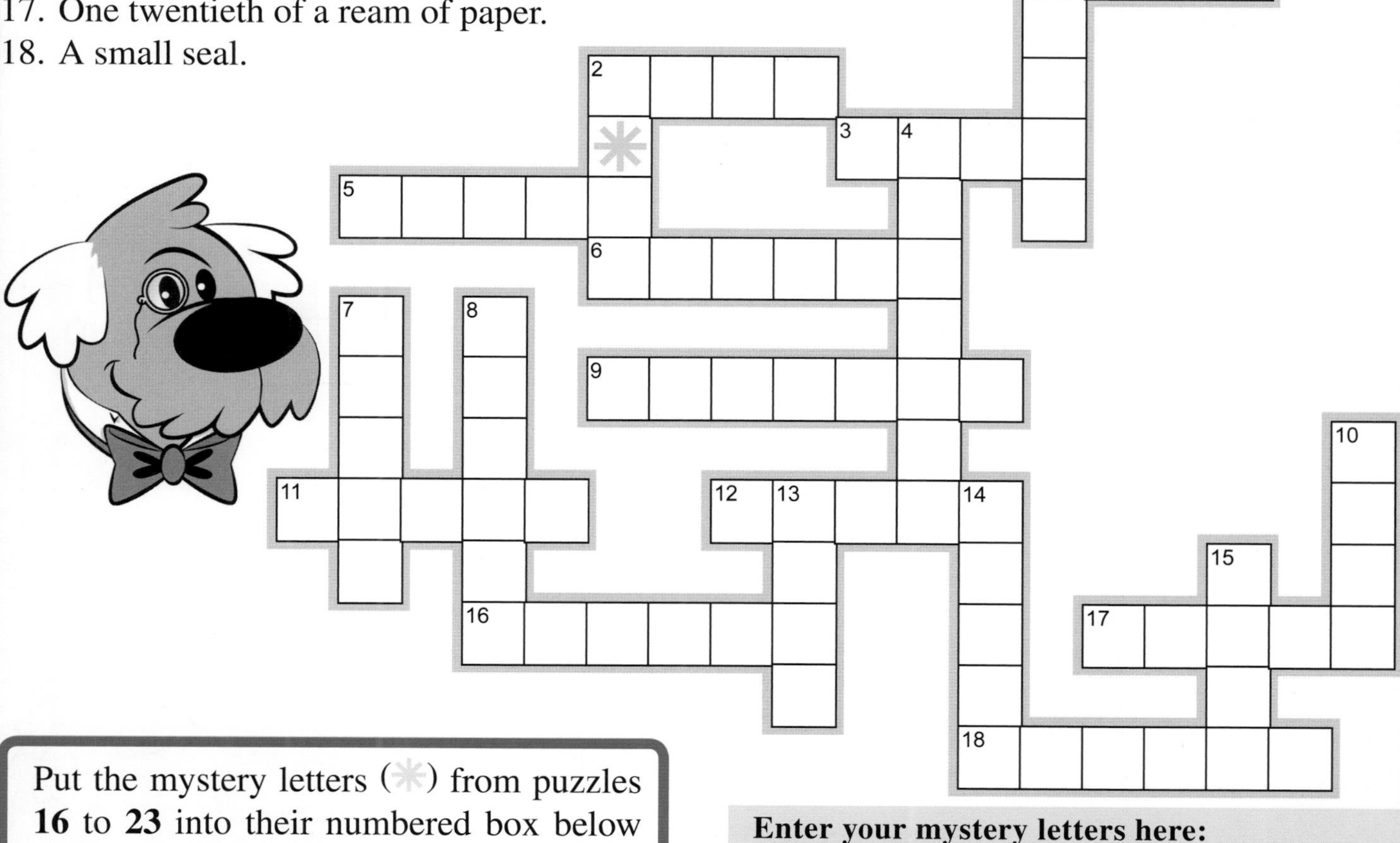

Put the mystery letters (✳) from puzzles **16** to **23** into their numbered box below then rearrange them to make **Dickens's Mystery Word**.
The clue is **OPTICIANS**.

Enter your mystery letters here:

16	17	18	19	20	21	22	23

Now rearrange them to make the:

Mystery Word:

Score / 20

wield
hair
road
whirred
canvas
knows
peal
vain
suede
suite
told
forth

Across

17

2. One of four parts.
6. Rung slowly and repeatedly.
7. Turned quickly.
10. Unit of language.
11. A mutual agreement.
12. Increase strongly and suddenly.
14. Change.
16. Swung back and forth.
17. Propelled a boat using oars.
19. Channel joining two seas.

Down

1. Organ of smell.
3. Large member of rabbit family.
4. Fruit or vegetable skin.
5. Turn a handle in a circular motion.
8. Eagle's nest.
9. Houses and land owned by medieval noblemen.
12. Tasting or smelling of sugar.
13. A rotating blade.
15. Asking people for their opinions.
18. An award for the winner.

Mystery Letter

Score

20

pries
manners
packed
altar
whined
airy
straight
serge

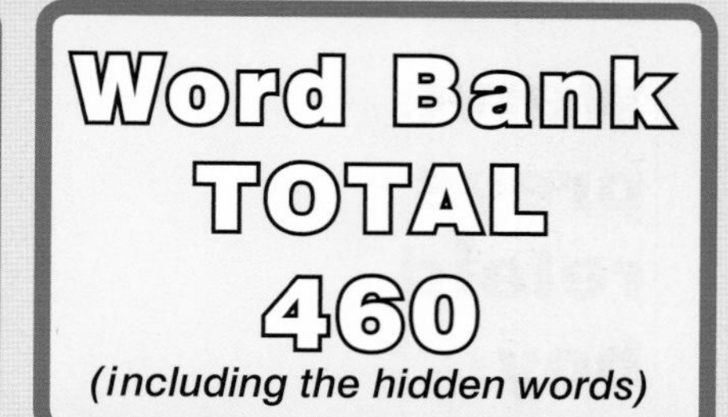

Exercise 17a

1) The lights came on when the electric generator word into life. ______________
2) They were delighted with the enormous hotel sweet. ______________
3) Monarchs often wheeled great power over their subjects. ______________
4) The colour of the hare on his head differed from that of his beard. ______________
5) The bride and groom emerged from the church to a peel of bells. ______________
6) "Guards! Bring fourth the prisoner so I may question him further." ______________
7) The addition of skylights made their loft bright and eyrie. ______________
8) Bread and wine of holy Communion stood on the alter. ______________
9) "I'm not to blame; I was tolled to dispose of the documents!" ______________
10) A coat made of surge should last a lifetime. ______________

Score / 10

Exercise 17b

11) The car boot is pact with everything we need for the holiday. ______________
12) The canvass tent was replaced as it was no longer waterproof. ______________
13) They searched everywhere for a replacement but it was all in vane. ______________
14) It's no longer a secret, everyone nose how the film ends. ______________
15) Her parents do not seem concerned about her appalling manors. ______________
16) The railway tracks stretched in a strait line way into the distance. ______________
17) The strong wind wind and moaned through the trees. ______________
18) Following the rowed seemed the best way to find their way in the fog. ______________
19) He uses a wire brush to buff his swayed shoes. ______________
20) "She's a busybody and prize into everyone's affairs." ______________

Score / 10

waive	**coward**	**lessen**
preys	**stake**	**use**
relaid	**flea**	**core**
boy	**hoes**	**bough**

Exercise 18a

1) It was a serious crash but nun of the passengers was seriously injured. ______________

2) News of the disaster did not phase her at all. ______________

3) He has an enormous appetite for such a small buoy. ______________

4) The boat's painter is securely tied to a steak driven into the ground. ______________

5) He was branded a cowered after he ran from the battlefield. ______________

6) The committee decided to wave the restrictions imposed last year. ______________

7) "I can't ewes this pen; it's run out of ink." ______________

8) After shouting so much supporting his team, he became quite horse. ______________

9) The Earth's corps is molten in parts. ______________

10) He is known as the Texan oil barren. ______________

Score /10

Exercise 18b

11) Taking his queue from the chairman, he began his presentation. ______________

12) She hates to see weeds in her borders so she hose them regularly. ______________

13) He took the dog into the garden and administered the flee powder. ______________

14) Their tour guide picked a bury and assured them it was edible. ______________

15) He used a chamois leather to wipe the due from the car's windows. ______________

16) The carpet had stretched badly and had to be relayed. ______________

17) Removing many non-essential items, we managed to lesson the load. ______________

18) The weight of the fruit was bending every bow on the tree. ______________

19) The bully praise on boys that are weaker than him. ______________

20) He always enjoys a current bun with his cup of tea. ______________

Score

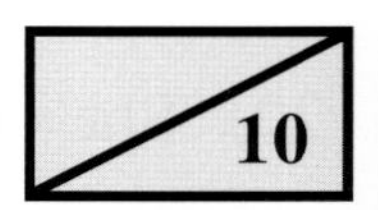

baron	**berry**
faze	**currant**
hoarse	**dew**
cue	**none**

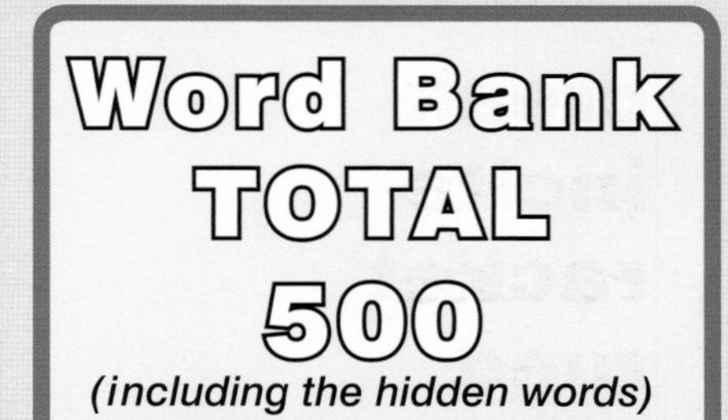

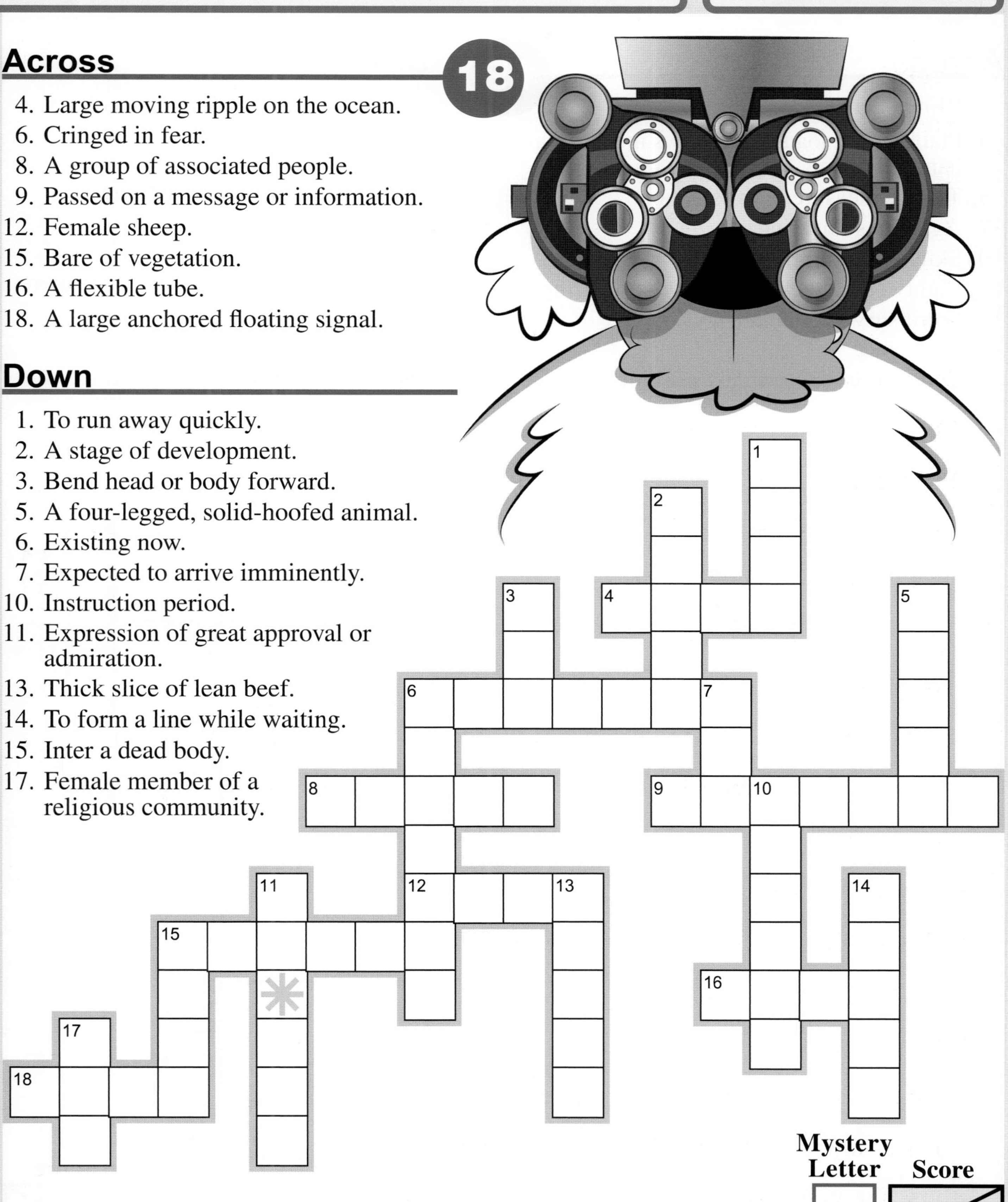

Across

4. Large moving ripple on the ocean.
6. Cringed in fear.
8. A group of associated people.
9. Passed on a message or information.
12. Female sheep.
15. Bare of vegetation.
16. A flexible tube.
18. A large anchored floating signal.

Down

1. To run away quickly.
2. A stage of development.
3. Bend head or body forward.
5. A four-legged, solid-hoofed animal.
6. Existing now.
7. Expected to arrive imminently.
10. Instruction period.
11. Expression of great approval or admiration.
13. Thick slice of lean beef.
14. To form a line while waiting.
15. Inter a dead body.
17. Female member of a religious community.

creak	**perse**	**aisle**
incite	**died**	**rye**
racket	**brews**	**sole**
rued	**callous**	**yoke**

Across

19

1. Ill-mannered.
3. Platform for loads that allows mechanical handling.
5. To give pleasure or satisfaction.
7. Agree to something.
10. Skin discolouration caused by injury.
12. Lightweight bat with a network of strings.
14. Spirit surviving death.
15. An island.
16. Transporting by animals working together.
17. The yellow of an egg.
19. A patch of thickened skin.

Down

2. Coloured by soaking in a colouring solution.
3. Draw lips together at the sides.
4. Damages by use or rubbing.
6. Legal inheritor.
8. Amusing and ironic.
9. To plant land with seeds once more.
11. Perceptiveness.
13. A stream that flows into a river.
18. Smallest amount possible.

Mystery Letter

Score

20

teeming
pleas
recede
air
leased
wares
ascent
palate

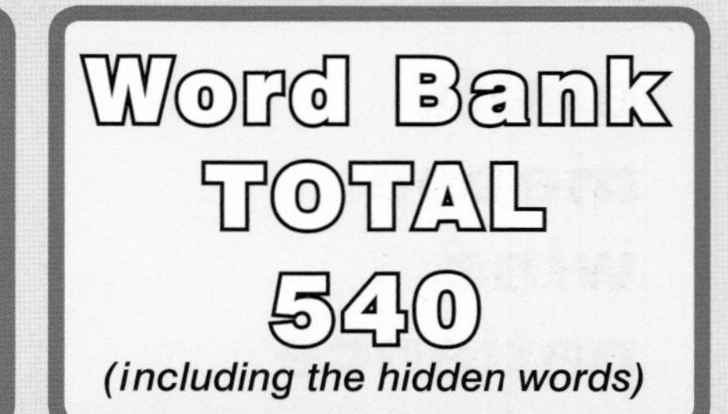

Exercise 19a

1) The coroner opened the inquest for the men who had dyed. _______________

2) Her promotion gave her soul responsibilty for the whole team. _______________

3) She spun round when she heard the floorboard creek. _______________

4) "Be sure to leave a wide isle between the rows of seats." _______________

5) Their scheme had failed and he rude the day he became involved. _______________

6) He plied his trade and sold his wears at local car boot sales. _______________

7) So much exposure to brutality left him callus and dangerous. _______________

8) A wine taster requires a very discerning pallet and nose. _______________

9) They began their assent of the mountain at dawn. _______________

10) "It's teaming outside; fetch a brolly!" _______________

Score 

Exercise 19b

11) The next day the bruise on her face had turned a shade of purse. _______________

12) She bruise a lovely cup of tea. _______________

13) It seemed to have vanished into thin heir and could not be found. _______________

14) The property was least immediately after it was advertised. _______________

15) They stood on deck and watched the land reseed in the distance. _______________

16) His intention is to insight the workers to take strike action. _______________

17) Every morning he would yolk the two draft animals together. _______________

18) "Stop making such a racquet; I can hardly hear myself think!" _______________

19) His favourite drink was a very small glass of wry whiskey. _______________

20) She was unmoved by their please for leniancy. _______________

Score 

chute	**stationary**	**paced**
moose	**mantel**	**side**
wine	**mustard**	**retch**
patience	**sty**	**coarse**

Exercise 20a

1) She stroked the pig and discovered its hair is very course. _______________

2) He asked the waitress for mustered to have with the roast beef. _______________

3) He asked the other fishermen what bate they were using. _______________

4) The old clock had stood on the stone mantle for many years. _______________

5) The oil spill, being non-missable, floated on the surface of the sea. _______________

6) The cyclist failed to stop and ran into the back of the stationery bus. _______________

7) Peering over the cliff edge, he saw it was a shear drop to the beach. _______________

8) "Would you prefer red or white whine with your meal?" _______________

9) The swimming pool has a water shoot and diving boards. _______________

10) Mucking out the pig stye is an unenviable job. _______________

Score /10

Exercise 20b

11) A short in the circuit caused the current to ark across with a flash. _______________

12) The heart is the hardest working mussel in your body. _______________

13) The football field is on the far sighed of the park. _______________

14) He walked from the start and paste out the distance to the finish. _______________

15) "You must learn to have patients and not act so hastily." _______________

16) She recommended to her friend the instructor who taut her to drive. _______________

17) It was necessary to sensor the letters sent home by service personnel. _______________

18) They were offered a lone to buy the car but they did not need it. _______________

19) The overpowering smell of rotting flesh made him wretch. _______________

20) Antelope, caribou and mousse are all types of deer. _______________

Score /10

loan
taught
sheer
miscible
muscle
bait
censor
arc

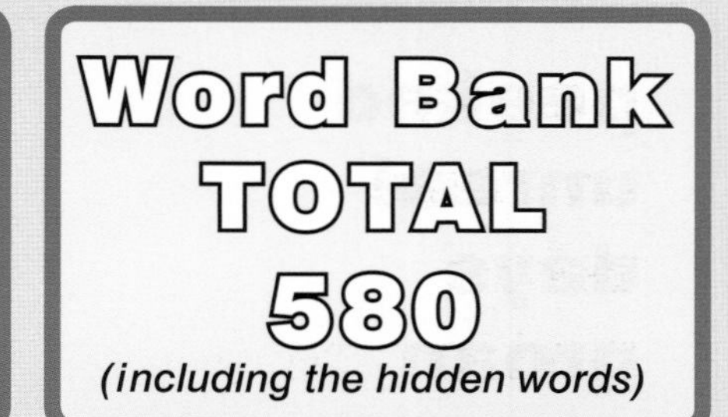

Across

2. Direction travelled.
7. Wire mesh in a gas lamp.
10. Fire a weapon.
12. Swelling on an eyelid.
14. To cut off.
15. Made an exhaling sound.
16. Stretched tightly.
17. Edible marine mollusc.
19. Noah's ship.
20. Could be avoided.

20

Down

1. To hold something back.
3. Things used for writing.
4. Light, sweetened dessert.
5. An adhesive mixture.
6. A detecting instrument.
8. People given medical treatment.
9. A person in trouble or distress who evokes pity.
11. Gathered people or things together.
13. Grumble peevishly.
18. Solitary.

peeked	**leak**	**root**
unreal	**earn**	**place**
days	**rough**	**eyelet**
groan	**peace**	**lea**

Across

21

2. Large, flat, edible seafish.
4. Very large and impressive.
6. Unwind.
7. A fancy pleated collar.
8. Caused somebody to be in a bad mood or feel resentful.
10. Edible plant.
12. Part detached from a larger whole.
15. Disgusting.
16. Perceived with the eyes.
17. A channel through which something flows.
19. Making something watertight or airtight.

Down

1. To pay for the use of something.
3. Audibly.
5. A way, path or road for travelling from one place to another.
9. A confused state.
10. Shelter from the wind.
11. Having developed and matured.
13. A small island.
14. Shallow depressions in a surface.
18. Vase for somebody's ashes.

Mystery Letter

Score

20

scene	**vial**
ceiling	**grate**
allowed	**higher**
ducked	**dense**

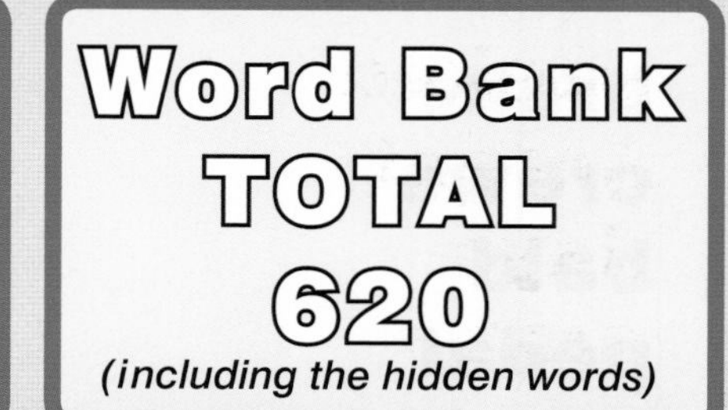

Exercise 21a

1) The firemen were blinded by the dents smoke throughout the building. _______________

2) Hanging from the high sealing are three huge chandeliers. _______________

3) You could hear the ship's timbers grown and creak in the swell. _______________

4) She remembers the daze before computers and mobile phones. _______________

5) To reach the guttering he had to climb hire up the ladder. _______________

6) "Don't make a seen, but I think they've scratched your car." _______________

7) The Piece Treaty of Versailles was signed on 28 June 1919. _______________

8) "Be advised that no-one is aloud to talk during the examination." _______________

9) At the interview, the candidate duct all the questions about her past. _______________

10) He took out a small vile and drank the contents. _______________

Score /10

Exercise 21b

11) He relied upon overtime to enable him to urn enough to live on. _______________

12) She opened the bedroom door and piqued in to check the children. _______________

13) The increase in income tax is the main route of their discontent. _______________

14) Gale force winds made for a very ruff sea crossing to Ireland. _______________

15) 'The lowing herd wind slowly o'er the lee'; from a poem by Thomas Gray. ___________

16) His constant criticising began to great on her. "Stop it!" she cried. _______________

17) The tapestry has a metal islet in each corner for easy hanging. _______________

18) "I was reading and lost my plaice when you interrupted me." _______________

19) The scene was unreel; the whole building was in flames. _______________

20) The company needs to plug the leek in its finances. _______________

Score /10

brake
crews
bald
pedal

cellar
profit
gilt
frees

passed
oar
waist
time

Exercise 22a

1) Down in the seller, the rats can be heard scrabbling around for food. ______________

2) He was unable to row with only one ore, so he paddled the boat instead. ______________

3) A jumbo guitar has a wider waste than a classical guitar. ______________

4) There is no thyme like the present to get things done. ______________

5) A very light knocking could just be herd above the engine noise. ______________

6) His defence lawyer asked for bale but the judge refused the request. ______________

7) "It's not a frog, it's a towed with dry warty skin." ______________

8) The job was not suitable for a school lever without work experience. ______________

9) On Sundays she would peddle five miles to her aunt's house. ______________

10) The gates, coated in guilt, looked magnificent. ______________

Score

Exercise 22b

11) "Use the break to slow the car before turning the corner." ______________

12) In its third year of trading the company began to make a prophet. ______________

13) After so many wet weeks they craved for an end to the reign. ______________

14) She searched through countless magazines for her ideal bridle gown. ______________

15) A squirt of penetrating oil often frieze a rusted nut and bolt. ______________

16) Although he had a beard, by the age of forty he was completely bawled. ______________

17) The Oxford and Cambridge cruise prepared for the start of the race. ______________

18) She crossed the road and past by on the opposite pavement. ______________

19) She worked like a Trojan and never seemed to tyre. ______________

20) With a smaller engine the van lax acceleration. ______________

Score

/10

tire	**leaver**
heard	**rain**
bail	**lacks**
bridal	**toad**

Word Bank TOTAL 660
(including the hidden words)

Across

22

2. Somebody predicting the future.
4. Culinary herb.
5. A large group of animals.
8. Circular rubber edging for a wheel.
10. Use carelessly and extravagantly.
12. A large bundle or package.
13. Legal culpability.
15. Harness for a horse's head.
16. Decorative band along a wall.

Down

1. A person offering something for sale.
2. To sell goods.
3. Mineral from which metal is extracted.
6. Beyond something.
7. A rigid bar used to move or lift a load.
8. Pulled along by rope or chain.
9. A pleasure trip by sea.
11. To rule a nation as its king or queen.
12. Separate into pieces.
14. Not strict or careful enough.
15. Shouted in a loud, aggressive voice.

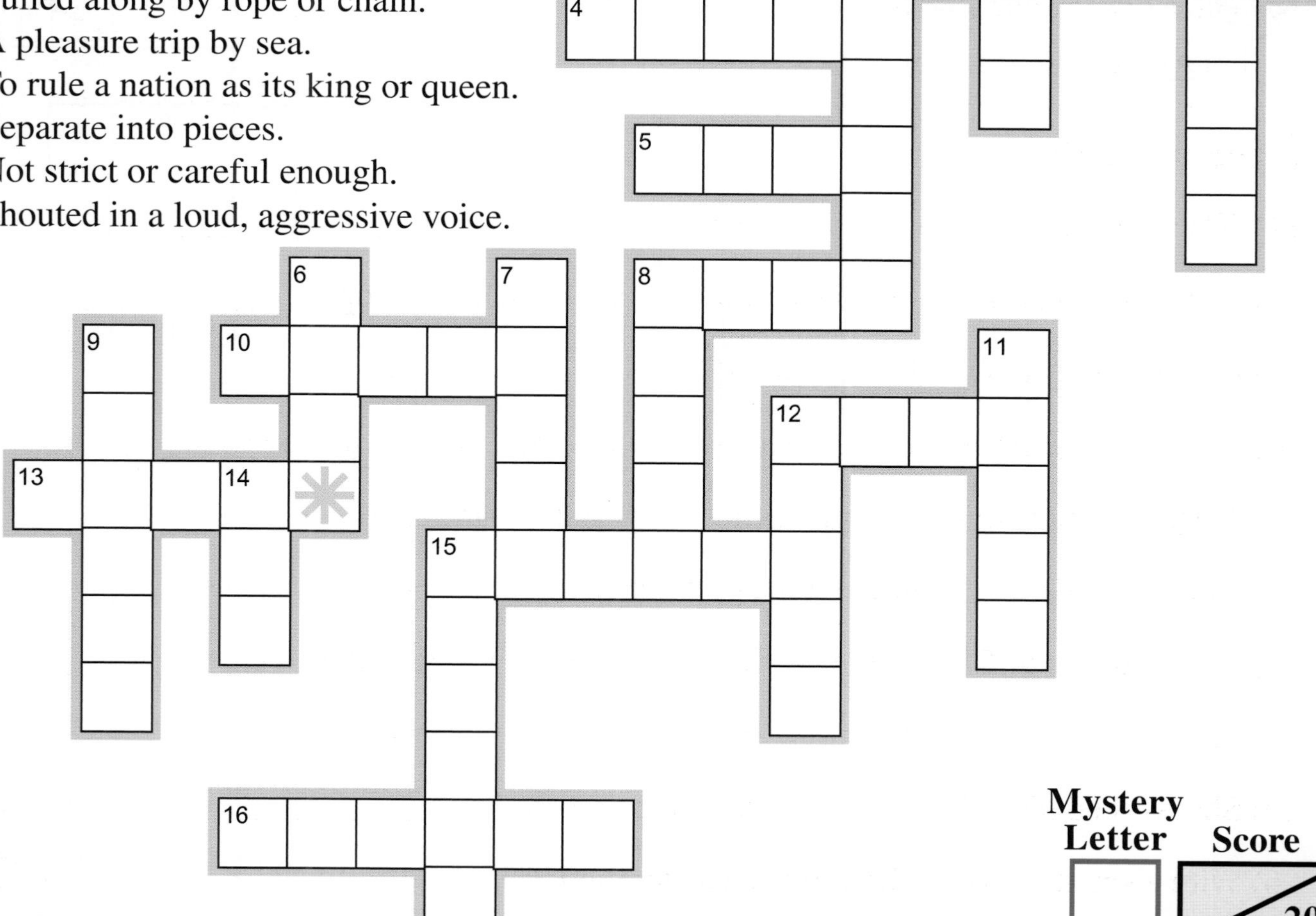

Mystery Letter

Score

20

serf	**rues**	**slay**
flair	**fir**	**frays**
steal	**find**	**complement**
scull	**humerus**	**tear**

23

Across

3. Funny, witty or amusing.
5. A grammatical string of words within a clause or sentence.
7. Foamy waves breaking on the seashore.
9. A clever trick to deceive others.
11. A sudden blaze of light.
14. A stand for a coffin.
15. Courage, spirit, or strength of character.
17. A current of cold air.
19. Painful or tender.

Down

1. To express sadness at somebody's death.
2. A statement to express praise and approval.
4. A waterside platform where boats are loaded and unloaded.
5. A piece of glass in a window.
6. Skeletal part of the head.
8. Soft dense coat on a hairy mammal.
10. Open snow vehicle pulled by horses.
12. A strong alloy of iron and carbon.
13. Punished by imposing a payment.
16. A colour.
18. A row of seats placed one above and behind each other.

Mystery Letter **Score** /20

! Don't forget to go back to page **33** and complete **Dickens's Mystery Word**.

beer
draft
soar
hew
key
morn
pain
metal

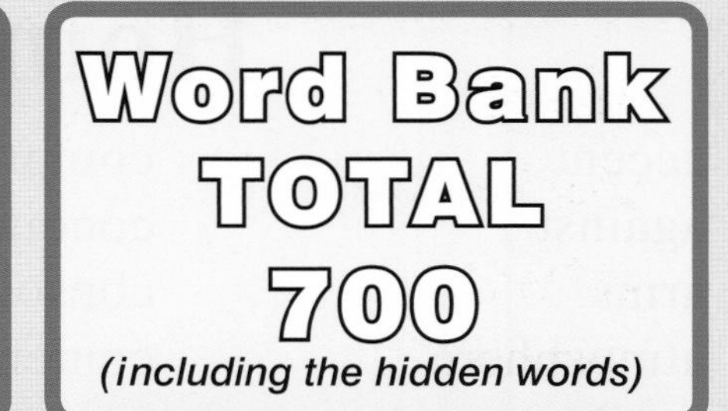

Exercise 23a

1) She wiped the tier from her eye and suppresssd a sob. _______________
2) "I've looked everywhere but can't fined my book anywhere." _______________
3) You need to wear gloves to pick up the sharp mettle swarf. _______________
4) I know he ruse the day he failed to take the job he was offered. _______________
5) At early mourn I went away with cheerful heart to work the day. _______________
6) Her tutor says she has a real flare for drawing and painting. _______________
7) Constant danger causes stress and phrase the nerves. _______________
8) He fell awkwardly and broke his humorous. _______________
9) A surf was little better off than an enslaved labourer. _______________
10) Knowledge and endeavour are the quay to success. _______________ **Score** /10

Exercise 23b

11) "Would you like a bier, or do you prefer a soft drink?" _______________
12) He is evidently in a lot of pane and needs medical assistance. _______________
13) The cones littered the ground at the foot of the fur tree. _______________
14) The sword St. George used to sleigh the dragon was named *Ascalon*. _______________
15) He placed his skull on the river and carefully climbed into it. _______________
16) The waiter recommended an exquisite wine to compliment the meal. _______________
17) It was only the first draught of the report and could be improved. _______________
18) The policeman saw him steel the bicycle from outside the library. _______________
19) They used a machete to hue a way through the jungle. _______________
20) Inflation caused prices to sore to unprecedented levels. _______________

Score

Homographs Word List

accent
against
arms
atmosphere
attribute
axes
back
ball
band
bank
bar
bark
bass
bat
batter
bear
bill
bit
bluff
blunt
board
boil
bolt
bore
bow
bowl
box
brush
buckle
buffet
cabinet
can
case
change
charge
chest
clear
close
coach
cobble
colon
commune
compact
company
compound
compress
conduct
console
content
contract
converse
coordinates
count
crane
date
defect
desert
digest
dip
discount
does
down
dress
duck
ear
entrance
evening
exploit
fair
fan
fast
fence
figure
file
fine
fire
firm
flounder
fly
foot
fork
frank
frequent
fresh
fuse
game
grave
gum
hail
hamper
handle
harbour
hard
hatch
head
hold
incense
incline
incomparable
initial
intimate
invalid
jam
junk
kid
kind
lap
late
lead
lean
learned
leaves
left
lie
light
like
live
loaf
log
loom
lounge
lumber
match
might
mind
mine
minor
mint
minute
mole
monitor
moped
nail
note
novel
number
object
organ
overlook
page
palm
park
patient
pawn
peer
pen
perfect
periodical
pitch
pitcher
plain
plane
polish
pound
present
press
proceeds
process
produce
project
prune
pupil
putting
quarry
racket
rare
rash
recall
refrain
refuse
reservation
right
ring
rock
rose
row
saw
scale
school
season

Homographs Word List

second
sentence
sewer
shed
ship
sign
sink
sock
soil
sole
solution
spare
spell
spirit
spring
spruce
squash
stable
staple
state
stern
store
strike
subject
suit
swallow
tap
tear
temper
temple
terrific
tip
trunk
upset
watch
wave
well
wind
wound
yard

Homophones Word List

adds / adze
ail / ale
air / heir
airy / eyrie
aisle / isle
allowed / aloud
altar / alter
arc / ark
ascent / assent
ate / eight
bail / bale
bait / bate
baize / bays
bald / bawled
band / banned
baron / barren
bean / been
beer / bier
berry / bury
berth / birth
billed / build
blew / blue
boarder / border
bough / bow
boy / buoy
brake / break
breaking / braking
brewed / brood
brews / bruise
bridal / bridle
callous / callus
canvas / canvass
caster / castor
ceiling / sealing
cellar / seller
censor / sensor
cereal / serial
cheap / cheep
chews / choose
choir / quire
chord / cord
chute / shoot
coarse / course
colonel / kernel
complement / compliment
core / corps
coward / cowered
creak / creek
crews / cruise
cue / queue
currant / current
cygnet / signet
cymbal / symbol
days / daze
dense / dents
dew / due
died / dyed
dough / doe
draft / draught
dual / duel
ducked / duct
earn / urn
eyelet / islet
faint / feint
fair / fare
faze / phase
few / phew
find / fined
fir / fur
flair / flare
flea / flee
forth / fourth
frays / phrase
frees / frieze
gait / gate
gamble / gambol
gilt / guilt
graft / graphed
grate / great
groan / grown
guessed / guest
guise / guys
hail / hale
hair / hare
hall / haul
hangar / hanger
heal / heel
heard / herd
hew / hue
higher / hire
hoard / horde
hoarse / horse
hoes / hose
hole / whole
humerus / humorous
incidence / incidents
incite / insight
intense / intents
jam / jamb
jibe / gibe
key / quay
knead / need
knows / nose
lacks / lax
laps / lapse
lea / lee
leach / leech
lead / led
leak / leek
leased / least
leaver / lever
lessen / lesson
links / lynx
loan / lone
made / maid
mail / male
maize / maze
manners / manors
mantel / mantle
marshal / martial
medal / meddle
metal / mettle
might / mite
miners / minors

Homophones Word List

miscible / missable
moan / mown
moose / mousse
morn / mourn
muscle / mussel
mustard / mustered
naval / navel
none / nun
oar / ore
ode / owed
one / won
overseas / oversees
paced / paste
packed / pact
pail / pale
pain / pane
palate / pallet
passed / past
patience / patients
peace / piece
peal / peel
pear / pare
pedal / peddle
peeked / piqued
peer / pier
perse / purse
place / plaice
pleas / please
plum / plumb
pole / poll
pore / pour
presence / presents
preys / praise
pride / pried
pries / prize
profit / prophet
racket / racquet
rain / reign
rays / raze
recede / reseed
receipt / reseat
reek / wreak
relaid / relayed
retch / wretch
road / rowed
roll / role
root / route
rough / ruff
rows / rose
rued / rude
rues / ruse
rye / wry
sail / sale
saver / savour
scene / seen
scull / skull
seas / seize
serf / surf
serge / surge
sheer / shear
side / sighed
sighs / size
sight / cite
sites / sights
slay / sleigh
sleight / slight
soar / sore
soared / sword
sole / soul
some / sum
stake / steak
stationary / stationery
stayed / staid
steal / steel
stile / style
storey / story
straight / strait
sty / stye
succour / sucker
suede / swayed
suite / sweet
summary / summery
taught / taut
tear / tier
teeming / teaming
tense / tents
threw / through
throws / throes
time / thyme
tire / tyre
toad / towed
told / tolled
tracked / tract
trussed / trust
unreal / unreel
use / ewes
vain / vane
vale / veil
vial / vile
wail / whale
waist / waste
wait / weight
waive / wave
war / wore
wares / wears
wax / whacks
weakly / weekly
wet / whet
whined / wind
whirl / whorl
whirred / word
wield / wheeled
wine / whine
wood / would
worst / wurst
yoke / yolk

Congratulations!

You have now learnt **700** homonyms; know what they mean and how to use them in a sentence.

We hope that you have enjoyed completing the series of books and that we have helped you increase your word power skills.

Answers

Exercise 1a

1) boil
2) mole
3) spirit
4) live
5) case
6) fly
7) pitcher
8) date
9) press
10) wave

Exercise 1b

11) brush
12) present
13) bluff
14) bar
15) rock
16) box
17) perfect
18) compound
19) clear
20) evening

Crossword No. 1

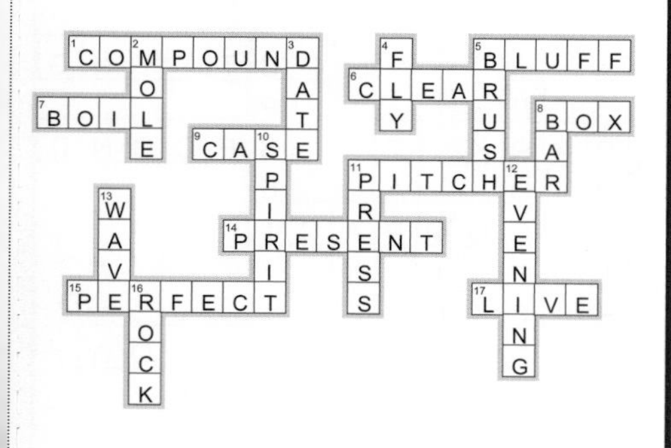

Letter = R

Exercise 2a

1) entrance
2) fine
3) sink
4) tip
5) number
6) lap
7) down
8) bat
9) attribute
10) hold

Exercise 2b

11) exploit
12) pupil
13) fresh
14) gum
15) count
16) change
17) minute
18) lead
19) ball
20) project

Crossword No. 2

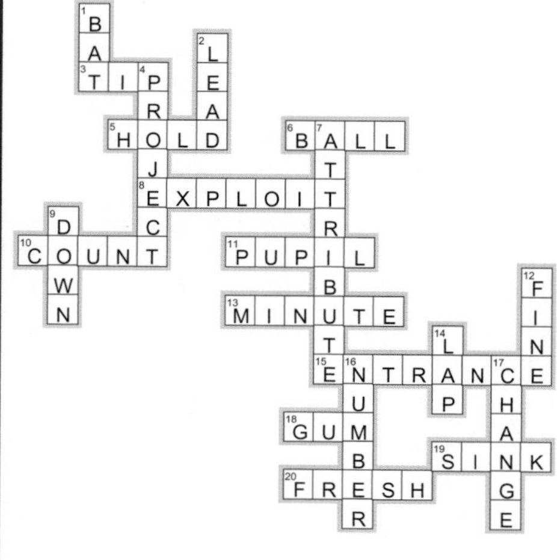

Letter = L

Exercise 3a

1) band
2) match
3) nail
4) moped
5) sewer
6) converse
7) wind
8) refuse
9) frequent
10) defect

Exercise 3b

11) page
12) incense
13) subject
14) arms
15) row
16) fast
17) ring
18) light
19) duck
20) bow

Crossword No. 3

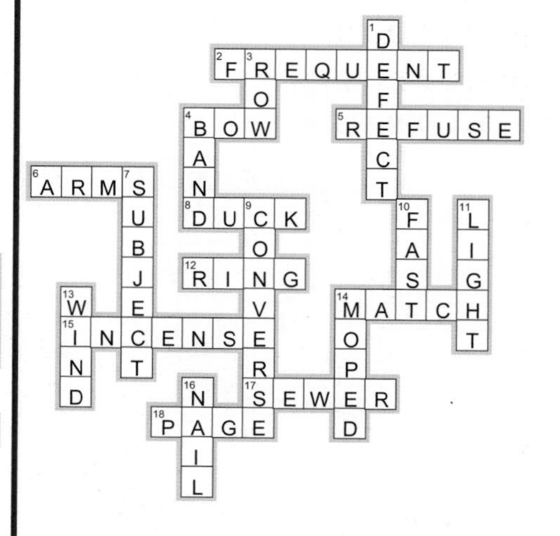

Letter = E

Answers

Exercise 4a
1) sock
2) can
3) lumber
4) compress
5) produce
6) content
7) racket
8) bass
9) discount
10) does

Exercise 4b
11) loaf
12) quarry
13) firm
14) bank
15) accent
16) overlook
17) back
18) buffet
19) colon
20) prune

Crossword No. 4

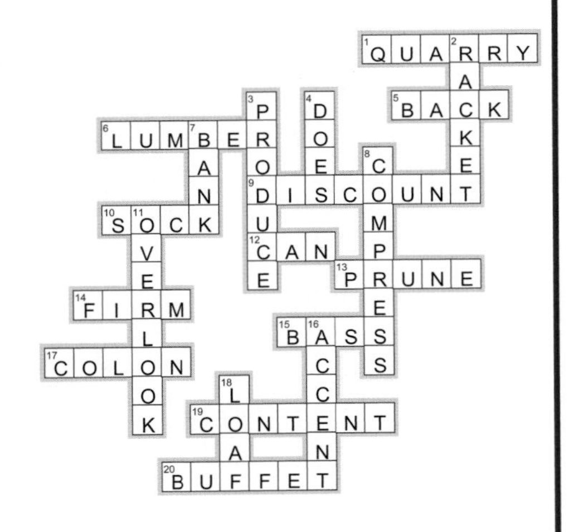

Letter = I

Exercise 5a
1) intimate
2) process
3) lean
4) commune
5) foot
6) wound
7) bear
8) coordinates
9) tear
10) pound

Exercise 5b
11) yard
12) invalid
13) well
14) learned
15) digest
16) jam
17) contract
18) recall
19) fan
20) conduct

Crossword No. 5

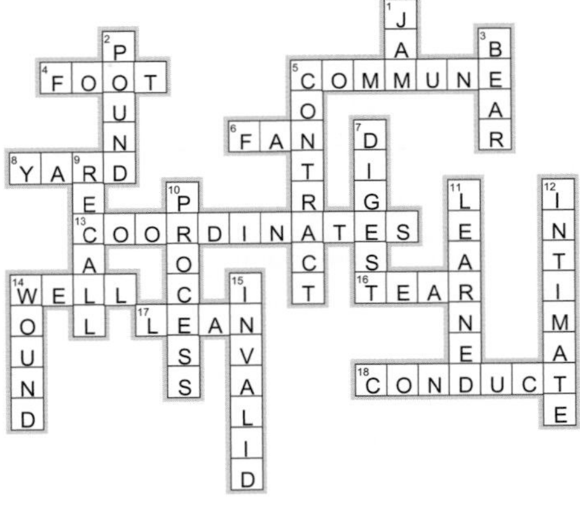

Letter = M

Exercise 6a
1) mind
2) rose
3) Polish
4) proceeds
5) console
6) park
7) second
8) compact
9) object
10) tap

Exercise 6b
11) incline
12) swallow
13) pen
14) left
15) lie
16) close
17) putting
18) axes
19) upset
20) desert

Crossword No. 6

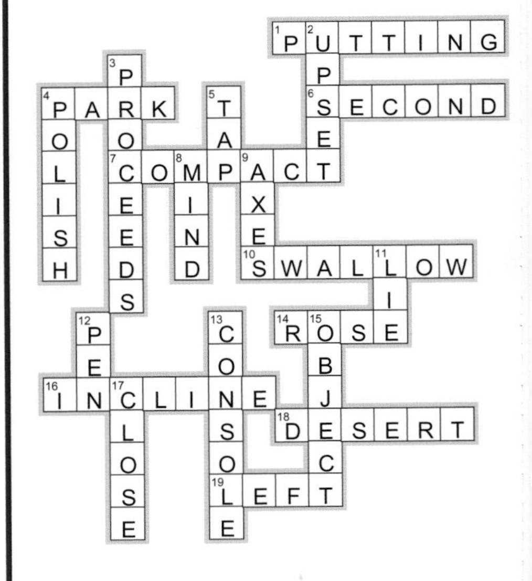

Letter = L

Answers

Exercise 7a

1) atmosphere
2) novel
3) company
4) monitor
5) frank
6) against
7) harbour
8) lounge
9) hamper
10) kid

Exercise 7b

11) loom
12) sentence
13) pitch
14) rare
15) sign
16) bore
17) bolt
18) staple
19) scale
20) buckle

Crossword No. 7

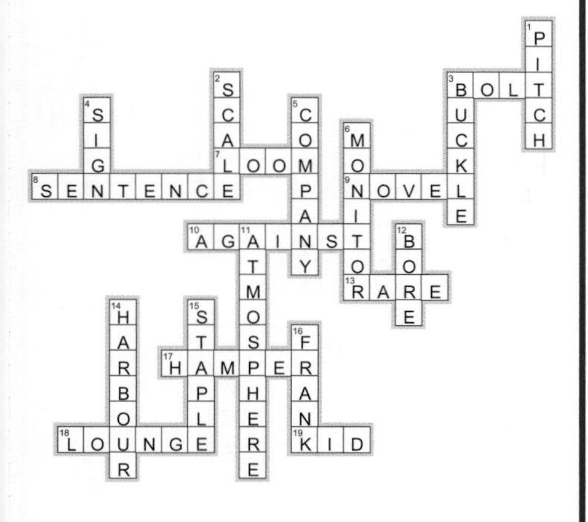

Letter = I

Exercise 8a

1) spring
2) pawn
3) bit
4) mine
5) bill
6) note
7) rash
8) dip
9) hail
10) fire

Exercise 8b

11) file
12) batter
13) soil
14) like
15) hard
16) state
17) initial
18) temper
19) fork
20) charge

Crossword No. 8

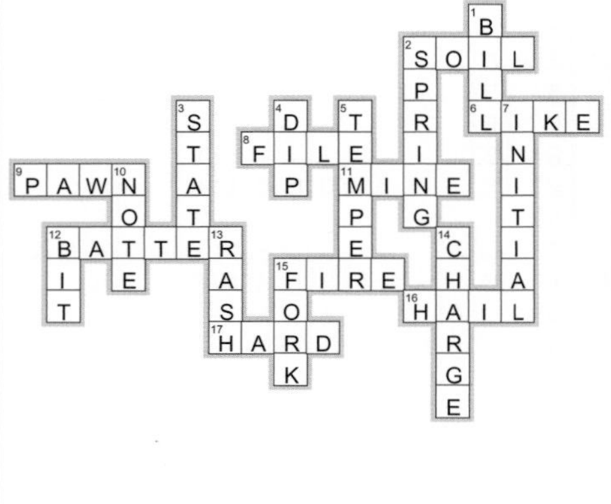

Letter = N

Exercise 9a

1) stern
2) school
3) season
4) flounder
5) fuse
6) minor
7) plain
8) bowl
9) store
10) saw

Exercise 9b

11) organ
12) hatch
13) grave
14) spare
15) periodical
16) terrific
17) spruce
18) might
19) chest
20) ear

Crossword No. 9

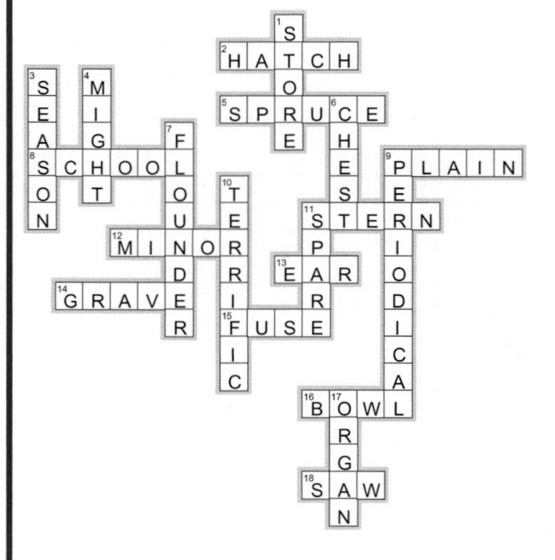

Letter = N

Answers

Exercise 10a
1) log
2) strike
3) solution
4) figure
5) shed
6) spell
7) watch
8) coach
9) board
10) refrain

Exercise 10b
11) late
12) mint
13) fair
14) temple
15) ship
16) fence
17) suit
18) crane
19) handle
20) sole

Crossword No. 10

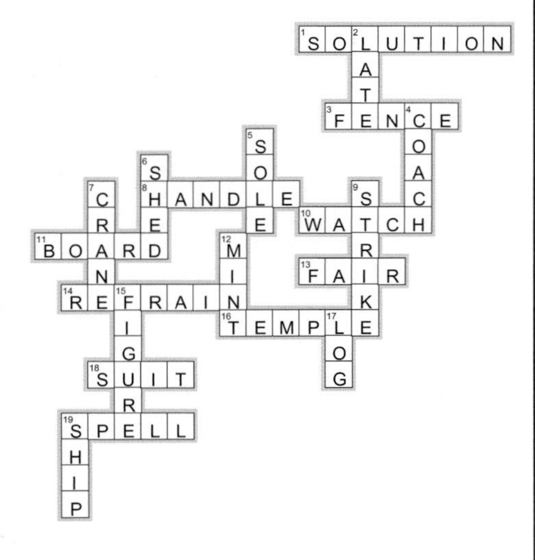

Letter = O

Exercise 11a
1) cobble
2) reservation
3) palm
4) junk
5) kind
6) game
7) blunt
8) patient
9) dress
10) plane

Exercise 11b
11) cabinet
12) bark
13) leaves
14) squash
15) trunk
16) stable
17) peer
18) head
19) right
20) incomparable

Crossword No. 11

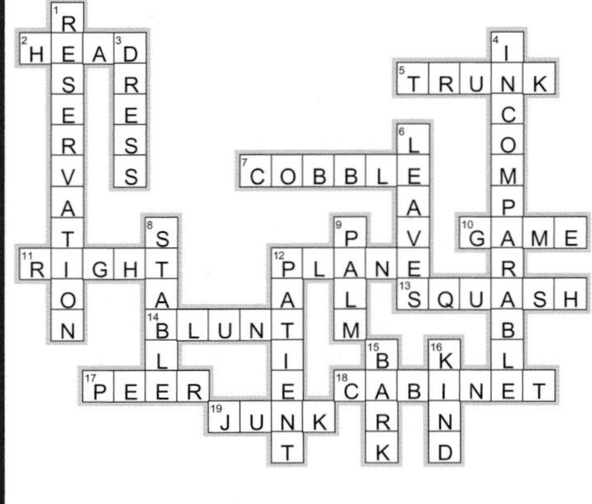

Letter = E

Exercise 12a
1) guest / guessed
2) phew / few
3) wore / war
4) savour / saver
5) gate / gait
6) border / boarder
7) whale / wail
8) wurst / worst
9) doe / dough
10) reseat / receipt

Exercise 12b
11) plumb / plum
12) maid / made
13) whet / wet
14) gambol / gamble
15) through / threw
16) mite / might
17) male / mail
18) leech / leach
19) whacks / wax
20) heel / heal

Crossword No. 12

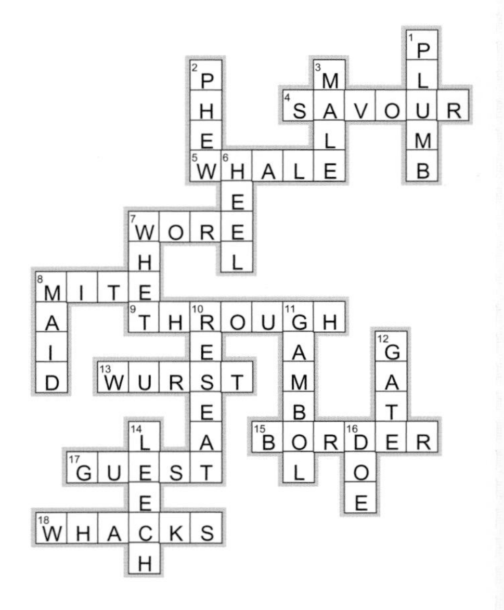

Letter = E

Answers

Exercise 13a

1) hanger / hangar
2) feint / faint
3) pour / pore
4) birth / berth
5) horde / hoard
6) pier / peer
7) maze / maize
8) duel / dual
9) tract / tracked
10) staid / stayed

Exercise 13b

11) meddle / medal
12) veil / vale
13) guys / guise
14) seize / seas
15) mown / moan
16) adze / adds
17) sights / sites
18) martial / marshal
19) raise / rays
20) presents / presence

Crossword No. 13

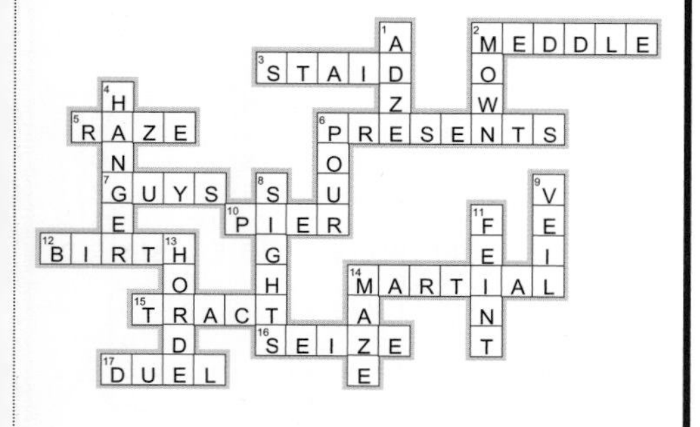

Letter = H

Exercise 14a

1) oversees / overseas
2) lapse / laps
3) rose / rows
4) pair / pear
5) hale / hail
6) whorl / whirl
7) fare / fair
8) whole / hole
9) jamb / jam
10) pale / pail

Exercise 14b

11) eight / ate
12) weight / wait
13) build / billed
14) led / lead
15) size / sighs
16) summery / summary
17) incidents / incidence
18) wreak / reek
19) banned / band
20) weekly / weakly

Crossword No. 14

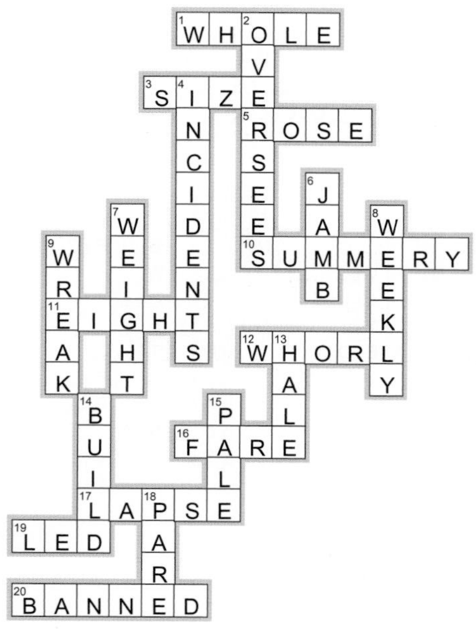

Letter = I

Exercise 15a

1) sucker / succour
2) won / one
3) sum / some
4) need / knead
5) haul / hall
6) been / bean
7) ale / ail
8) choose / chews
9) cord / chord
10) navel / naval

Exercise 15b

11) would / wood
12) owed / ode
13) cheep / cheap
14) lynx / links
15) style / stile
16) castor / caster
17) kernel / colonel
18) throed / throws
19) graphed / graft
20) symbol / cymbal

Crossword No. 15

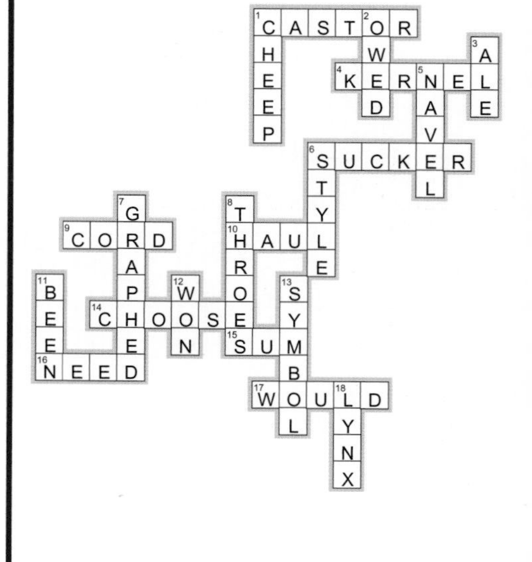

Letter = R

Answers

Exercise 16a
1) minors / miners
2) blue / blew
3) sword / soared
4) story / storey
5) bays / baize
6) tents / tense
7) intents / intense
8) poll / pole
9) trust / trussed
10) sale / sail

Exercise 16b
11) signet / cygnet
12) role / roll
13) serial / cereal
14) gibe / jibe
15) braking / breaking
16) cite / sight
17) slight / sleight
18) brood / brewed
19) pried / pride
20) quire / choir

Crossword No. 16

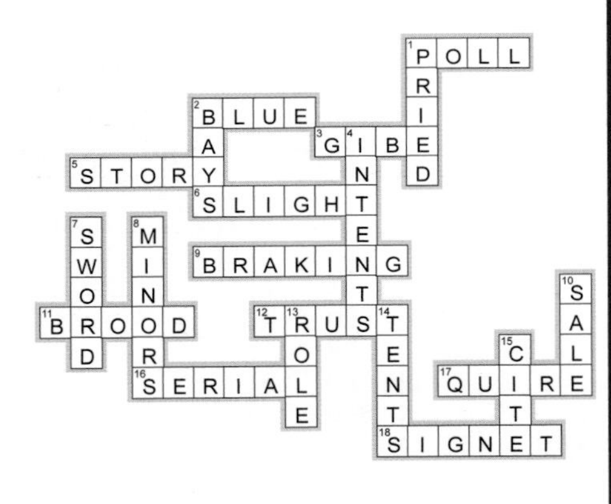

Letter = A

Exercise 17a
1) word / whirred
2) sweet / suite
3) wheeled / wield
4) hare / hair
5) peel / peal
6) fourth / forth
7) eyrie / airy
8) alter / altar
9) tolled / told
10) surge / serge

Exercise 17b
11) pact / packed
12) canvass / canvas
13) vane / vain
14) nose / knows
15) manors / manners
16) strait / straight
17) wind / whined
18) rowed / road
19) swayed / suede
20) prize / pries

Crossword No. 17

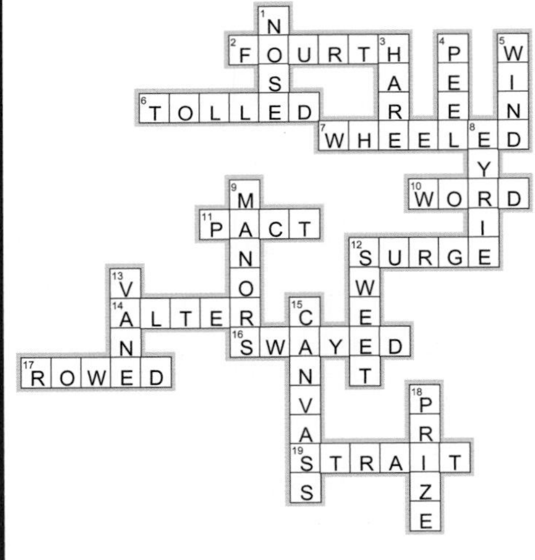

Letter = R

Exercise 18a
1) nun / none
2) phase / faze
3) buoy / boy
4) steak / stake
5) cowered / coward
6) wave / waive
7) ewes / use
8) horse / hoarse
9) corps / core
10) barren / baron

Exercise 18b
11) queue / cue
12) hose / hoes
13) flee / flea
14) bury / berry
15) due / dew
16) relayed / relaid
17) lesson / lessen
18) bow / bough
19) praise / preys
20) current / currant

Crossword No. 18

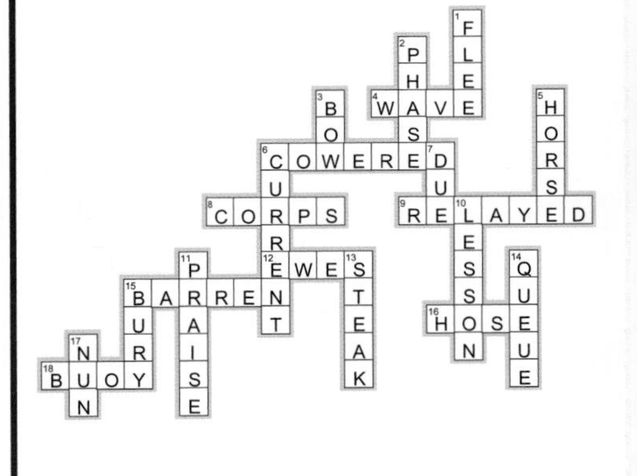

Letter = A

Answers

Exercise 19a

1) dyed / died
2) soul / sole
3) creek / creak
4) isle / aisle
5) rude / rued
6) wears / wares
7) callus / callous
8) pallet / palate
9) assent / scent
10) teamimg / teeming

Exercise 19b

11) purse / perse
12) bruise / brews
13) heir / air
14) least / leased
15) reseed / recede
16) insight / incite
17) yolk / yoke
18) racquet / racket
19) wry / rye
20) please / pleas

Crossword No. 19

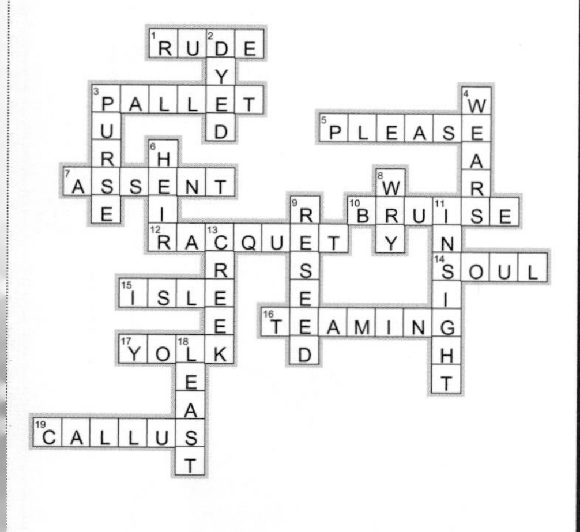

Letter = T

Exercise 20a

1) course / coarse
2) mustered / mustard
3) bate / bait
4) mantle / mantel
5) missable / miscible
6) stationery / stationary
7) shear / sheer
8) whine / wine
9) shoot / chute
10) stie / sty

Exercise 20b

11) ark / arc
12) mussel / muscle
13) sighed / side
14) paste / paced
15) patients / patience
16) taut / taught
17) sensor / censor
18) lone / loan
19) wretch / retch
20) mousse / moose

Crossword No. 20

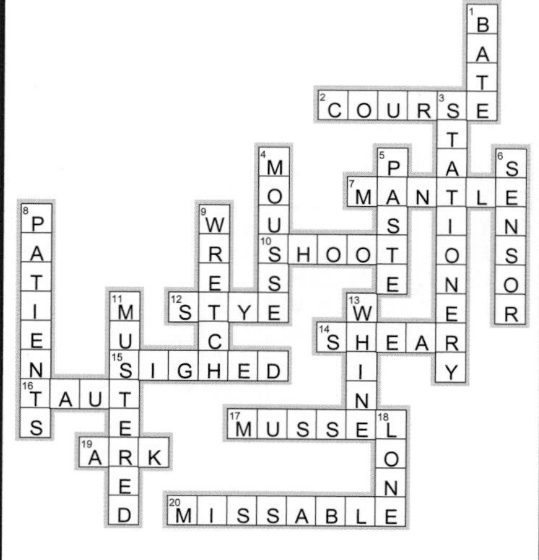

Letter = C

Exercise 21a

1) dents / dense
2) sealing / ceiling
3) grown / groan
4) daze / days
5) hire / higher
6) seen / scene
7) piece / peace
8) aloud / allowed
9) duct / ducked
10) vile / vial

Exercise 21b

11) urn / earn
12) piqued / peeked
13) route / root
14) ruff / rough
15) lee / lea
16) great / grate
17) islet / eyelet
18) plaice / place
19) unreel / unreal
20) leek / leak

Crossword No. 21

Letter = C

Answers

Exercise 22a

1) seller / cellar
2) ore / oar
3) waste / waist
4) thyme / time
5) herd / heard
6) bale / bail
7) towed / toad
8) lever / leaver
9) peddle / pedal
10) guilt / gilt

Exercise 22b

11) break / brake
12) prophet / profit
13) reign / rain
14) bridle / bridal
15) freeze / frees
16) bawled / bald
17) cruise / crews
18) past / passed
19) tyre / tire
20) lax / lacks

Crossword No. 22

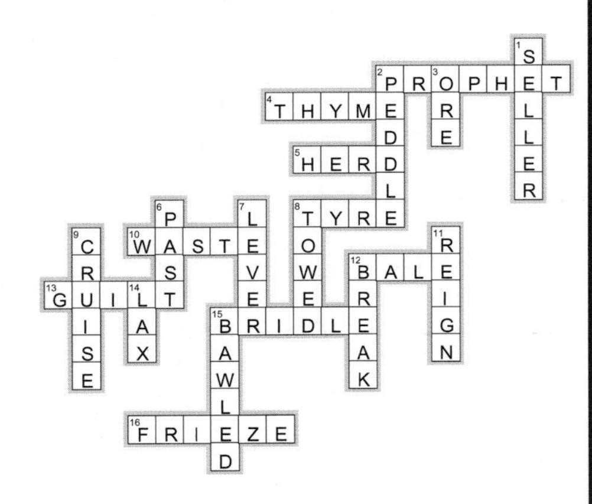

Letter = T

Exercise 23a

1) tier / tear
2) fined / ind
3) mettle / metal
4) ruse / rues
5) mourn / morn
6) flare / flair
7) phrase / frays
8) humorous / humerus
9) surf / serf
10) quay / key

Exercise 23b

11) bier / beer
12) pane / pain
13) fur / fir
14) sleigh / slay
15) skull / scull
16) compliment / complement
17) draught / draft
18) steel / steal
19) hue / hew
20) sore / soar

Crossword No. 23

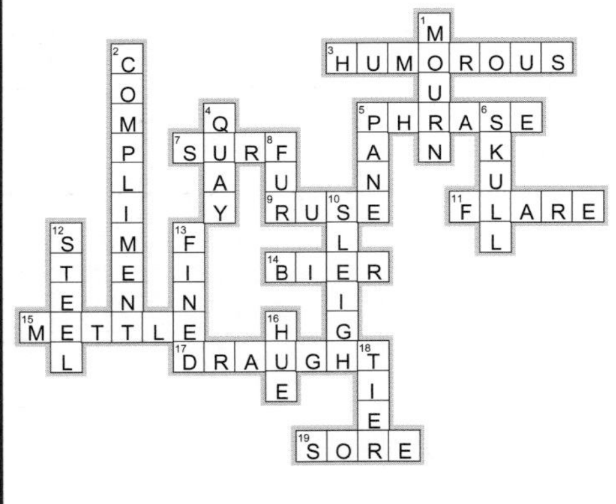

Letter = A

PROGRESS CHARTS

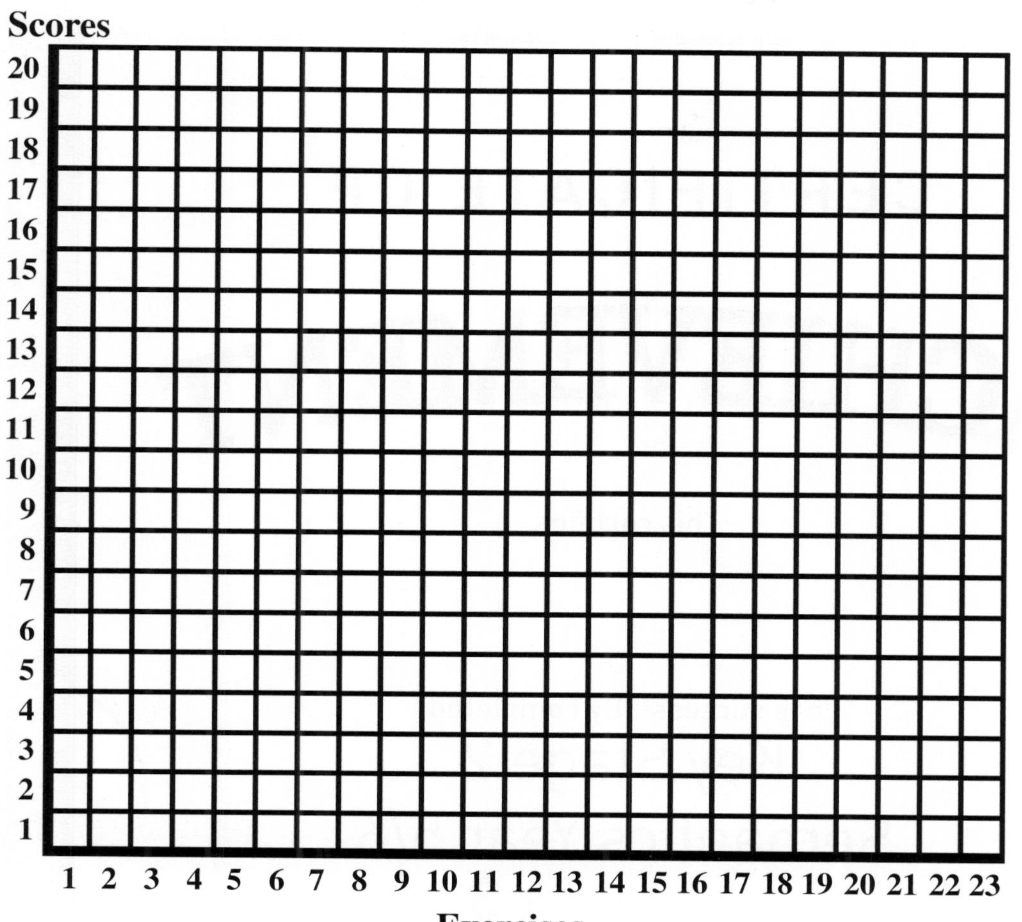

Shade in your score for each exercise on the graph. Add them up for your total score out of 460. Ask an adult to work out the percentage.

Total Score

Percentage

% A

Scores

20 19 18 17 16 15 14 13 12 11 10 9 8 7 6 5 4 3 2 1

1 2 3 4 5 6 7 8 9 10 11 12 13 14 15 16 17 18 19 20 21 22 23

Crosswords

Shade in your score for each crossword on the graph. Add them up for your total score out of 460.

Total Score

Percentage

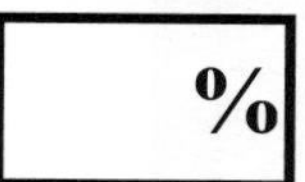

B

For the average percentage add %A and %B and divide by 2

Overall Percentage

%

CERTIFICATE OF

ACHIEVEMENT

This certifies

____

has successfully completed

Key Stage 2

Semantics Year 5/6

WORKBOOK **3**

Overall percentage score achieved [ ] %

Comment ______________________________

____

Signed ______________________________
(teacher/parent/guardian)

Date ______________________________